**OFFICIALLY
DISCARDED**

The World of the Bison

LIVING WORLD BOOKS
John K. Terres, Editor

The World of the
Bison

With Text and Photographs by

Ed Park

J. B. Lippincott Company
Philadelphia and New York

ISBN-0-397-00624-1
Third Printing
Printed in the United States of America
Library of Congress Catalog Card Number: 76–77868

To my parents, Mr. and Mrs. H. N. Park, for introducing me to our natural world, and to my wife, Ruth, for enjoying it with me now

Contents

Introducing the Bison

FRENCH *voyageurs,* who were among the first white men to explore North America, called the large, humpbacked animals they encountered on the plains *les boeufs,* meaning oxen or beeves. Through the normal sequence of word corruption, *boeuf* became the English "buff," then "buffle" or "buffler," and finally "buffalo."

Scientists use the Latin name *Bison bison* for this creature, pointing out that its correct common name is "bison." The true buffalo, they say, has no hump, explaining further that that name belongs only to the water buffalo in Asia and the African buffalo—animals belonging to the genus *Bubalus.*

Nevertheless, to most Americans the bison is a "buffalo" and probably always will be, although some people call it the American buffalo, the American ox, or even just plain buff.

Regardless of the name by which we know it, the bison is a truly impressive beast. Largest of the land animals of North America, the bulls stand around six feet high, measuring from the ground to their highest part—the hump; the cows about five feet; some bison are even larger. In length, males measure nine to twelve feet; females, between seven and eight feet. Bison are powerfully built animals with broad, massive heads; short, thick necks; high humped shoulders; small hindquarters; and short legs. Both the male and the female have sharp curved horns and a short tasseled tail.

13

The World of the Bison

I have seen bison bulls, using their heads like battering rams, thrust their way through strong woven-wire or heavy timber fences with little hesitation. In his work in Wood Buffalo National Park, in Canada, J. Dewey Soper, a Canadian naturalist, told of frightened bison running through thick timber "with about the same abandon as in the open. When close-herded, they ride rough-shod over everything in their path, trampling down shrubbery, crashing over windfall and often levelling dead standing trees up to six inches in diameter."

The bison's horns are short and thick at the base, tapering quickly to a sharp point and curving outward and upward from the sides of the head. They are hollow and permanent, being formed over a bony core that is an extension of the cranial frontal bone. The horns of a three-month-old calf are mere black stubs, only about an inch long. They continue to grow throughout the life of the animal, slowing in growth in later years. Abnormalities of various kinds occur, and it is not unusual to see a bison with an abnormal horn. Bison love to rub and scratch; this

The horns on a five-month-old calf give little hint of their future size.

The bull above is probably rubbing his head on the ground to relieve an itch. The horn at right is damaged by years of rubbing.

including rubbing the head upon the ground. Consequently, the horns of old animals have a definite flattening on the outer curves, where they have been worn by years of rubbing.

As bulls grow older, the outer layers of the horn begin to break off near the tip, and very old bulls may have only blunt stubs, with just a small, sharp point in the center of each stub.

The horns of bulls are much more massive than those of cows and have a basal circumference 75 to 100 per cent greater than that of females of the same age. Horns of an adult bull in his prime are smooth, glossy, and sharp, making them wicked weapons when deftly used in close combat.

Visitors to Yellowstone National Park can see the largest set of bison horns on record. The museum at Fishing Bridge, Wyoming, has on display the skull of a huge bull killed in Yellowstone National Park in 1925. The outside spread measures 35⅜ inches, and the longest horn measures 23¼ inches along the outside curve. These two measurements, representing the greatest spread and the longest horn length ever measured in bison, place the animal in number-one position in the official Boone and Crockett Club book, *Records of North American Big Game*.

The Fishing Bridge museum skull registers a maximum basal circumference of the largest horn at 16 inches and a spread between horn tips of 27 inches. While great, these measurements are not the largest ever recorded. The number-two animal in the record book, from the Northwest Territories of Canada, registered a massive basal circumference of 18½ inches on both of its horns. The animal listed in thirty-first place in the record book, from Alaska, registered the greatest tip-to-tip spread: 29¾ inches. However, these are maximum measurements from outstanding animals, and an average adult bull has horns nearer to 18 inches long, with a basal circumference of 13 inches.

There are two subspecies, the plains bison and the wood bison. The plains bison, with which we are most familiar, once covered the vast

A massive head, a shaggy coat, and powerful hindquarters give the bison an impressively rugged appearance.

Great Plains of North America. The larger and darker wood bison lives in northern Alberta and the Northwest Territories in Canada.

The pattern and extent of hair growth greatly add to the bison's rugged appearance. The head, neck, front legs, and fore part of the body are covered with a thick mantle of long dark hair. The longest growth is on the forehead, where the hair can sometimes measure nearly two feet in length. The back half of the body is covered with much shorter hair, thus making it seem as if all of the bison's strength is in the front half of the body. The hindquarters, however, are not as weak as they look.

Various hair measurements were taken from an old bull now preserved in the National Museum in Washington, D.C. He had been killed in early December, when the bison's coat is at its best. The hair measured 16 inches on the forehead, 8 inches on the breast, 10½ inches on a fore-leg, 3¾ inches on the shoulders, 6½ inches on the top of the hump, 2 inches on the middle of the side, and 1¾ inches on the hindquarters. The tuft on the tail was 19 inches long.

Most of the year the hair is a rich chocolate brown, shading to black in some places. During the winter and spring the pelt is bleached to a lighter yellowish brown. Once in a great while a bison is born with unusual coloration, usually a grayish, bluish, or cream color. On April 10, 1967, a very dark charcoal-gray bull calf was born on the ranch of Harry Pon of Burns, Oregon. I saw the youngster three days later, and his nearly black color made him stand out from the other calves. Rarest of all is the white bison. As far as I have been able to determine, there are no white ones alive today.

The bison's hump is a distinctive feature that makes the creature readily identifiable. It is formed by the elongation of the dorsal spines of the thoracic vertebrae. Examination of a split carcass would reveal that the bison has fourteen pairs of ribs, compared to the thirteen pairs of domestic cattle. It would also soon become evident that the skeletal structure probably makes it impossible for the bison to raise its head above the level of the shoulder. It can, however, tilt its muzzle upward— a typical position when the animal is bellowing.

The bison's skull in general is massive and shows the strength characteristic of this animal. There is a substantiated report of a bull being shot in the head, from the front, with a .30/06 rifle, at a distance of about ten yards, and having the bullet bounce back as a flattened piece of lead, without apparent damage to the bison.

A bison's ears are visible just behind the horns and are most easily seen

The bison uses its well-padded head as a battering ram.

on calves, cows, or bulls with short hair on the head.

The eyes of bison are dark brown with an irregular pear-shaped iris a little over an inch in its longest measurement. It has been said that their position makes it easy for a man on foot to dodge the bison's charge, since the animal cannot see straight ahead. This is not true: only the rear vision is blocked. A quick look into the face of a bison which is facing directly toward you will show very clearly that both eyes are visible.

The nose, like so much of the bison, is big and broad, with large nostrils. It is black, as are the outer lips. The inner lips and tongue are

19

The bison frequently uses its tongue to clean its nose.

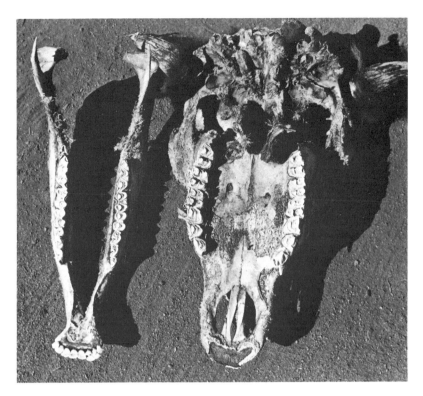

Eight incisor teeth in the lower jaw can crop grass closely. The massive molars and premolars grind the food.

bluish-purple. The tongue is used often to clean the nostrils; one deft sweep into each nostril does the job.

The bison's teeth are similar to those of our domestic cattle. The upper jaw lacks incisors and canine teeth but has three premolars and three molars on each side. The lower jaw contains eight incisors in front but no canines, and has three premolars and three molars on each side.

Like our domestic cattle, the bison is a grazing animal, and its tooth structure is adapted for nibbling grass and grinding it. Being a ruminant, it swallows its food partly chewed and later regurgitates it in small masses, called "cuds," and chews it more thoroughly at its leisure. The food passes through a complicated four-chambered stomach, consisting of the rumen, reticulum, omasum, and abomasum.

An adult bull has a long black beard some 8 to 12 inches long. His

It is easy to see why some people think a bison looks like the Devil incarnate.

horns, dark coloration, and fierce power have led people to liken him to the Devil in appearance.

The bison's senses of sight, hearing, and smell vary from poor to very acute. Of the three, sight seems to be the poorest, though this may be open to debate. Bison have a highly developed sense of smell and keen hearing. When startled but unable to determine the direction of possible danger, bison face into the wind and try to pick up any airborne scents that they can identify. A stationary herd can hear the approach of another herd many minutes before any sounds can be heard by a human listener.

While observing and photographing bison in various areas, I have often found it simpler to approach from downwind, even if this has meant crossing open country within their view. Not until I have got quite close have they seemed to become concerned. However, any unnatural sounds, such as the metallic clank of cameras banging together, has usually caused them to leave in a hurry.

On the other hand, I have noticed heads turn in my direction when I've appeared over a ridge—downwind from the herd but still quite a distance away. During one trip to the National Bison Range in western Montana, I noted that some heads looked my way when I walked into the open a good half-mile away from them.

Robert C. Fields, Refuge Manager of Fort Niobrara National Wildlife Refuge in Nebraska, wrote me that "they can spot us when we ride into the pasture on horses from a distance of two miles. Maybe this is not good but it is pretty fair. It is true that when they get running they do not seem to do too well at seeing but appear to be able to see quite well as a general rule."

Bison are gregarious animals, apparently greatly enjoying being in a crowd. They are usually found in herds numbering from a few animals up to the hundreds. Only very old bulls, like sullen old men, prefer the solitary life.

23

Being gregarious, bison live and travel in herds.

In temperament the bison is *usually* peace-loving and quiet, sometimes even lazy—except during the mating season. This is a troubled time for most animals, and they must fight for supremacy among themselves in order that the best of the species may be perpetuated. There is one word that can best characterize the bison's temperament: unpredictable. A peacefully grazing animal, seemingly content with the job of filling its belly, can and will attack almost anything without any warning or apparent reason. Many persons have been badly gored by animals they have bottle-fed and lovingly cared for from infancy.

When you watch a grazing or resting herd of bison, it is difficult to imagine their doing any harm, but some of our country's earlier naturalists, who studied the bison when it still numbered in the millions, rated it a very dangerous animal: "a savage buffalo should be treated the same as a tiger" . . . "second only to the brown bear on this continent as a

Only very old bulls prefer a solitary life.

potential killer" . . . "probably killed more people than all the carnivores put together." One of these men, Ernest Thompson Seton, considered the bison even more dangerous than the grizzly.

Although the bison is generally able to cope with its environment, its mentality, by human standards, is considered low grade. For example, a bison will walk into quicksand that has already trapped the other animals ahead of it. Or it will stop feeding and run headlong into a train that happens to come along as the animal tries to join the main herd across the track. A hunter could kill an entire herd of a hundred animals without moving from one spot because the bison apparently cannot comprehend danger in a puff of smoke and the crack of a rifle. Its limited intelligence is pointed to as a principal cause of its near-extinction, but its decline was more likely owing to its inability to adapt to such "civilized" things as the high-powered rifle and man's usurpation of the bison's range. This species proved long ago that it could survive and prosper in its native habitat: probably nowhere else on earth—not even in wildlife-rich Africa—has one large mammalian species ever attained such large numbers as did the bison of North America. It must be remembered that, for untold centuries, this powerful creature feared nothing. No animal on the continent could best the bison bull in a fair fight.* Thus it is perhaps not so surprising that the bison never learned to fear the gun.

One of the most deceptive things about the bison is its ability to move with speed. We normally see it calm and undisturbed—lying down, standing motionless, or walking slowly. It moves very slowly while feeding or plods along at a not much faster pace when heading for water or a buffalo wallow or when merely seeking a change of scenery. It gives the

*Editor's Note: The only North American animal powerful enough to challenge a large bison bull was the grizzly bear, which weighed perhaps half as much as the bison. The relationship of these two animals in the wild is discussed in the Living World series book *The World of the Grizzly Bear,* by W. J. Schoonmaker.

The front and hind hoofs of a large bison.

appearance of being quite clumsy, as if it could not move rapidly if it had to. But this is pure deception. When in a hurry or when pursued or pursuing, the bison is fast and quick on its feet and has great endurance. The literature is full of instances of herds running for many miles without apparently tiring, of outrunning teams of horses, or of outlasting relays of good saddle horses.

The bison is cloven-footed; its hoofs are very much like those of domestic cattle. It has four gaits—walking, trotting, galloping, and bounding. The walking gait is used most of the time, and the feet are moved in this order: right rear, right front, left rear, left front.

A bison often finds it necessary to trot for a short distance on a sharp downhill grade. It also uses this gait when it is in a hurry. Its two diagonally opposite feet move at the same time: right front and left rear together, left front and right rear together.

Viewed head on, a herd of bison on the run can be an especially frightening sight.

Despite their protruding tongues, these running bison are not tired.

When in a very big hurry, bison move into a gallop. The feet move in this sequence: right front, left front, right rear, left rear. For the bison, this is a high-speed gait. It spreads its hind legs well apart, like a horse, and throws them well out in front of the front feet. When the animal is at full speed, the hind feet come up on either side of the head. A big bull weighing a ton and moving at a full gallop is an awesome sight. An entire herd thundering along at high speed is enough to make most people quake, especially if they have a head-on view of the action. After the animals run some distance, their tongues stick out, giving them the appearance of being tired, but they have great endurance.

I have tried several times to clock running bison with a car speed-ometer, but each attempt failed. The plains across which they were mov-ing was so rough that I could not drive fast enough to keep up with them. I have also chased them down roads in Wood Buffalo National Park, Canada, but they always turned aside, into the safety of the timber. However, others have successfully timed bison at speeds of about 35 miles an hour for a half mile.

The fourth gait is the bound, similar to the bounding of a mule deer, when all legs are moved simultaneously. It seems to be an awkward gait, most generally a play behavior in bison, although I have seen them use it when being pursued by men on horses.

As a matter of fact, bison closely pursued by men on horseback display surprising agility and quickness. At the National Bison Range in Mon-tana, I watched the annual roundup in October of 1967. As is customary, all the bison were driven into corrals for a complete tally of the herd. Calves were branded and vaccinated, brands on the rest were checked, and those to be sold or slaughtered were cut out into separate pens.

During these operations there is much activity, and a person can see for himself the real speed and agility of a harassed bison. I watched experienced men who know how to ride and who know bison habits being completely outmaneuvered by bison that were able to wheel and cut more quickly at high speed than the horses could. Once in the smaller corrals, some bison showed a quickness of head and foot that would hardly be suspected of peacefully grazing animals.

To move the bison from one corral to another, the roundup workers tie a few cans to the end of long bamboo poles and shake them at the animals. The rattling noises are sufficient to drive the bison through the gates, but there are always a few animals—especially the older bulls—that don't scare easily. If the cans are rattled too near a bull's head for his liking, he will hook at them with his shiny black horns, leaving no one in doubt about the speed and force of his responses. Cans rattled near his tail also invite his wrath—and make anyone watching think twice about getting near those powerful hind legs. Clearly, in close fighting, an angered bison bull would be a deadly adversary, and I was reminded of the more aggressive fighting bulls I have seen in Mexico's bull rings.

The most common sound that bison make is a grunt, not unlike that of a barnyard pig. It is often used to maintain contact between individuals in a herd, including that between a cow and her calf—a low grunt here, another over there. If a bison makes this same sound while advancing, it can be interpreted as a minor threat or a question. Many times I have worked my way slowly out into the middle of a herd in order to watch and listen. Now and then a lone animal would walk toward me, stop a few yards away, and grunt. I got the impression that it was a questioning sound; possibly the bison was trying to establish my motives for being

Clearly, this bull considered me an intruder.

there. No aggressive action followed the inquiry, though there was always a possibility that the animal would decide to force me to leave immediately.

There is a sound that can be definitely considered a threat, although one of only medium intensity. It is a snort, a sharp, quick sound that has been reported to come only from bulls. It is most likely to be heard from the dominant bull in a group when another bull intrudes, and can be considered a vocal sparring or challenge. If an approaching bull makes this sound, it is wise to retreat gracefully.

The bellow is the real warning signal. This growling, guttural roar is unmistakable in meaning. With head tipped upward, mouth open, lip upcurled, and tongue protruding, the animal appears to be grimacing. Bison bellow more frequently during the peak of the rutting season, but it is also used any time an animal feels aggressive. Cows occasionally bellow, as do bulls that are merely ruminating or wallowing. Regardless of the season or the occasion, each time I have seen and heard bulls bellowing I have looked around quickly for an escape route.

Bison reach maturity when they are seven or eight years old. Their average life span is about fifteen or twenty years, although a few individuals have been known to live thirty or forty years. Ed Olson, Superintendent of Wood Buffalo National Park, wrote me that the herds contain officially aged animals thirty-eight years old.

As yet, no completely successful methods have been established for determining the age of bison. In recent years much work on aging has been done with other species that involves weight of the eye lens. This method has proved unreliable with bison after the first four and a half years, because in this species the eye lens grows rapidly until that age and then remains fairly constant. An experienced observer can give a rough estimate of a bison's age by examining horn conformation and development, but this is not accurate enough to be satisfactory.

A bison's bellow is unmistakable in meaning.

Tooth wear is also used as a means of calculating age in a few species and helps to determine age to some extent in the bison, but the results are only fair. Too often, the kinds of food the animals eat can cause a deviation from the expected amount of wear.

Tooth replacement has proved an excellent means of aging bison, but again only up to the age of four and a half. After that, the most accurate means so far discovered is by laboratory examination of tooth growth.

33

This, of course, requires specialized equipment and is therefore not a field technique.

Like so many things connected with the wildlife of this continent, man did not consider it particularly important to record observations of bison until its original range had been greatly reduced. By carefully studying journals kept by early explorers, by examining bones picked up in excavations or dried lake beds, and by checking other sources, we have slowly pieced together the full extent of that range.

The main center of bison population was the vast Great Plains of North America, stretching from Mexico into Canada. Lesser numbers lived along the Atlantic seacoast, in the Appalachian Mountains, the Rocky Mountains, and almost to the Pacific Coast.

Except for Alaska, Arizona, Hawaii, Michigan, and the New England States north of New York, every state in the United States has yielded evidence of being once inhabited by bison. Even this statement is still open to dispute. For example, there is some evidence to substantiate the presence of bison at one time in Arizona. And until an old journal was discovered in 1936 which mentioned bison in Florida and Alabama, it was not believed they ever frequented those areas. Also, though some writers say bison never appeared in Nevada, there is a Buffalo Meadows, on Buffalo Creek, in Washoe County in northwestern Nevada, and a few bison bones have been found in recent years in other areas of that state.

In Canada the animal inhabited all areas except the northeastern provinces and western British Columbia. In Mexico it lived in what are now the states of Chihuahua, Coahuila, and Nuevo León.

In the United States today, the bison no longer exists in a free, wild state except for a few hundred animals in Arizona, Utah, and Alaska. All the rest are in private herds, zoos, parks, or refuges. There is, however, a wild herd, numbering possibly 17,000 animals, in or near Wood Buffalo National Park in northern Alberta and the Northwest Territories of

Canada. It is the largest free-roaming herd in the world, and it lives mostly within a park.

Wood Buffalo National Park cannot be called a park in the normal sense. The largest one in the world, covering 17,300 square miles, it is unfenced, being merely an area laid out by lines on a map. The largest national park in the United States is Yellowstone, which covers 3,419 square miles—less than one-fifth the area of the Canadian park. To compare it another way, Wood Buffalo National Park is more than one third the area of, say, Alabama, New York, Mississippi, or Pennsylvania.

My first visit to the park, in the summer of 1966, was by airplane, because there was no road into it. However, one was completed in the fall of that year, and I was able to drive there in the summer of 1967. Even now, most of the park is still impenetrable by car. In this huge wilderness the bison roam freely, as they have done for centuries—and are preyed upon by wolves, as they have been for centuries. Also echoing the past are the few thousand bison outside the park that the Indians, as part of their heritage, are permitted to hunt.

Those who know the history of the bison can take pleasure in knowing that there is a place somewhere in this world where these majestic creatures can wander as they please.

The Bison in History

BEFORE THE COMING of the white man, bison numbering in the millions roamed the plains and woods of a large portion of North America. Estimates, all of which must be considered educated guesses, varied greatly; the vast numbers involved are difficult to imagine. Furthermore, most of these "censuses" were made long after wholesale slaughter began.

Many early reports made no attempt to estimate the size of the herds but merely used phrases such as "teeming myriads," "countless herds," or "incredible numbers." But then naturalists, conservationists, and others began to wonder how many there had been before the white man arrived, and the great guessing game began. Most estimates seemed to place the number at 60 to 75 million, with some running as high as 125 million. No one suggested less than 50 million bison.

The difficulty with counting, or even imagining, such numbers can be demonstrated by a historical case on record, as reported by Martin S. Garretson in *The American Bison: Story of Its Extermination and Its Restoration Under Federal Protection*:

Mr. Robert M. Wright, a well-known citizen of Dodge City, Kansas, who had lived for 50 years in the heart of the buffalo country and who in 1866 was appointed post trader at Fort Dodge, told the writer that one night General Sheridan and Major Henry Inman, having just made the trip from Fort Supply, were occupying his office at Fort Dodge. They called him in to discuss how many buffalo there were between Fort Dodge and Fort Supply.

The buffalo were moving north and it was known that the great herd extended more than 100 miles in width and was of unknown length.

Taking a strip fifty miles east and fifty west over the trail by which they had come, they first estimated ten billion animals. General Sheridan said, "That won't do!" They figured it again and made it one billion. Finally they reached the conclusion that there must be considerably over 100 million, but said they were afraid to give out these figures lest they might be accused of something worse than prevaricating. Nevertheless they believed the last number to be a conservative one.

Ernest Thompson Seton, the highly respected early-day naturalist, attempted to calculate the numbers by various methods, taking into consideration the total acres of bison range and the logical stocking rate of the various habitats within that range, allowing for seasonal movements, and making comparisons with domestic livestock stocking rates. He estimated that there were between 50 and 75 million. His soundest estimates placed the number at about 60 million or slightly higher.

For the sake of an illustration, let us use the figure 63,115,200 as the number of bison before the white man. Most of us cannot comprehend this large a number of anything, including huge shaggy beasts grazing contentedly on the wide-open plains. But just how large is 63,115,200? Imagine a long, single-file column of bison, head to tail, walking past you, one every two seconds. Take a counter and start counting them— one every two seconds, hour after hour, day after day—without pause.

During the first minute 30 bison would file past; in the first hour 1,800 would go by. If you could stay awake for the first twenty-four hours, you would count 43,200 bison. The days would roll by and sometime during the twenty-fourth day the one millionth bison would hurry past.

Months would drag by, the seasons would change, and you would become tired of counting. Bison adding up to several millions would have passed before your eyes in seemingly endless file, with still more to come. At the end of the first year your counter would show a total of 15,768,000

The bison seemed to the Indians especially designed to meet all their needs.

bison. But the end would not be in sight!

The second year would pass, then the third, and finally the fourth, with even an extra day added for a leap year. As the *fourth* year drew to a close, the last bison would hurry by, and you could look at your counter one last time! 63,115,200!

Now you can begin to comprehend the unbelievable numbers of bison our continent once held.

The Indians shared this land with bison, deer, pronghorn, and many other species; from them they obtained food, clothing, and shelter. For the Plains Indians, the bison was the actual basis for existence. Probably nowhere else at any time has a people depended so completely on one species for its existence.

As long as the bison were there, the Plains Indians prospered. They utilized literally all parts of the bison except its bellow. The flesh, either fresh or dried, was eaten. The hide was turned into robes, moccasins, clothing, tepee coverings, shields, ropes, boats, and even coffins. The bison's long hair served as ornamentation or was braided into rope. The bladder, stomach, and other internal parts made excellent containers for storing pemmican, nuts, or berries. The bones were used in the construction of bows, scrapers, and other tools; the tough sinews for thread, bowstrings, and webbing on snowshoes. Ribs formed the runners of dog-drawn sleds. Bones also made good toys for Indian children. Horns were fashioned into drinking vessels, spoons, and ladles or were employed to carry hot coals from one fire to start another. The bison's hoofs were used to make glue, fat provided hair grease, and the gall was an important ingredient in making yellow paint. In addition, many of these parts played a role in important ceremonies.

When water holes dried up, Indians—and, later, white men—survived on the juices from the stomachs of slain bison. Even the animal's excrement was used in its dried state for fuel. On the treeless plains, the "buffalo chip" was often the only fuel available for cooking or warmth. These chips are practically impervious to weather, last for years, and make a hot fire.

Thus it is easy to see why the bison featured so prominently in many of the Indian's superstitions, legends, and dances and why the red man fought when he saw the white man begin to exterminate the herds.

White bison were sacred to the Plains Indians. These albinos were exceedingly rare: estimates derived from the records of hide traders indicate that a white bison appeared only about once in every five million

The famed white bison, "Big Medicine," now on display in the Montana Historical Museum, in Helena. (Photo by Babe May.)

animals. The Indians looked upon them as the special property of the sun god, and when one was killed, its meat was left untouched, its hide given a place of high importance, and its tongue cured and presented to the sun god with prayers.

The most famous white bison in modern times was a bull named Big Medicine which lived for twenty-six years at the National Bison Range in Montana. He died in 1959 and is now mounted in the Montana Historical Society Museum in Helena, Montana. His genes must have gone to Alaska with twenty-three animals shipped there from the National Bison Range to start the Alaskan herd, because the only two white bison reported anywhere since Big Medicine are two calves from Alaska, both of which died at an early age.

Various Indian tribes used rituals to attract the bison or to guide the hunters to the herd. The Blackfeet used special songs; the Mandans presented food to a bison head. Several tribes used bison skulls in dances and rituals designed to attract the living animals; others captured and then released a horned lizard, believing that it would scamper off in the direction of the nearest herd. According to others, a raven that circled the camp site, cawed, and then flew away was also flying toward the closest herd.

Although Indians employed chants, prayers, rituals, and dances either to attract or to point the way to the bison, they relied fully on their own abilities when it actually came to killing the big brutes. As hunters, they were skillful and imaginative, though their weapons were primitive and, before the white man brought them, they had no horses. They had to depend on their wits and whatever materials were available.

Indians were not particular how they killed the animals, and we in our well-fed existence might think some of their methods unsporting. But when one is hungry and there's a half ton of good meat walking around, anything goes. The means they used depended entirely upon the situation. The bow and arrow worked well if a herd could be closely stalked from downwind. A few animals resting in a brushy draw might also be approached closely enough to permit use of the bow, or even a spear.

In winter, Indians donned snowshoes so that they could outmaneuver their quarry in deep snow and bring them down with arrow or spear. Fortunately for the hunters, the bison's great size could be taken advantage of: a number of animals were slowly driven out onto a frozen river; then the Indians closed in from all sides, causing the bison to bunch up. Often it was just a matter of time before the ice gave way under their weight. The animals, swept downstream under the ice, would drown, and the Indians would then proceed to an open area farther downstream and pull the carcasses out of the water.

Sometimes a large number of Indians would surround a herd, beginning some distance away to avoid stampeding the bison immediately, and then tighten the ring until they were close enough to attack. In the ensuing panic, many animals were killed—and more than one hunter got trampled.

Indian hunters also built elaborate impoundments with fences made of brush, rocks, or anything else handy. To force the bison toward the enclosure, they built wings of brush and rocks that fanned out from the entrance and then drove the herd slowly forward, sometimes from a great

Indian hunters felled stampeding bison with arrow or spear.

distance. Once the animals were inside, other hunters concealed nearby launched their attack.

One of the most spectacular means of killing bison, and one which has been depicted in some colorful paintings or dioramas, was the use of the "buffalo jump," or *pishkun,* as the Indians called it. This was a cliff at the end of a relatively large, flat plain. The height varied, but it was always high enough to kill or cripple an animal falling from it. Again wings were built to channel the hapless beasts to the edge of the cliff.

A large herd would be started in the right direction and then stampeded by the Indians. In full flight, the bison would head for the brink. The poor-sighted creatures in the lead became aware of the danger too late; though they tried to stop, the weight and sheer mass of the other animals following behind would force the leaders over the cliff. In turn, the rest would plunge to their deaths.

Such a mass killing may have been hideous, but it was an efficient way to obtain tons of meat, and the Indians adopted this method whenever they could. *Pishkuns* were probably used wherever the terrain was suitable; however, most of them seem to be in Montana, Wyoming, and Colorado, often along the breaks of a stream or a river.

Not surprisingly, these jumps have in modern times yielded a vast treasure of Indian artifacts and bison bones, affording archaeologists a further insight into history. At the base of some cliffs the bones are many feet deep, indicating their use as buffalo jumps for countless years.

I have visited a few of these cliffs, and, standing at the edge, I conjured up the image of vast herds, driven by yelling hunters behind, hurtling thirty, forty, or sixty feet to perish on the rocks below.

Once the white man introduced the horse, the hunting methods of the Plains Indians changed. Mounted, they could ride into a herd, select a running animal, and, moving along beside it, accurately put an arrow into its chest at a distance of only a few feet. When eventually firearms became available to the Indians, they no longer had much difficulty getting food.

44

The buffalo jump, or pishkun, *near the Madison River in Montana, is one of the most spectacular jumps in the United States.*

But while the white man's horse and gun made bison hunting easier for the Indians, they also made the animals more available to the white man. The destruction of the vast bison herds in North America has been described as the most remorseless and ceaseless slaughter of wild animals in all history.

In 1521, Hernando Cortez was the first European to see an American bison, at the palace of Montezuma, the great Aztec ruler, in Anáhuac, now Mexico City. A Spanish historian of the time, De Solis, reported:

In the second Square of the same House were the Wild Beasts, which were either presents to Montezuma, or taken by his Hunters, in strong Cages of Timber, rang'd in good Order, and under Cover: Lions, Tygers, Bears, and all others of the savage Kind which New-Spain produced; among which the greatest Rarity was the Mexican Bull; a wonderful composition of divers Animals. It has crooked Shoulders, with a Bunch on its Back like a Camel; its Flanks dry, its Tail large, and its Neck cover'd with Hair like a Lion. It is cloven footed, its Head armed like that of a Bull, which it resembles in Fierceness, with no less strength and Agility.

But the bison Cortez saw was a captive animal, at least 300 miles south of its natural range. It was not until nine years later, in 1530, that another Spanish explorer, Alvar Nuñez Cabeza de Vaca, saw the bison in its natural habitat. After being wrecked on the Gulf coast, he wandered inland and westward and caught sight of a few bison in what is now southeastern Texas.

In 1542 Francisco Vásquez Coronado was possibly the first European to see the bison in the great numbers we associate with this animal. Entering what is now Arizona, he traveled eastward through New Mexico and into Oklahoma, a land "full of crooked-backed oxen."

In the 1600s a steady stream of Europeans made their way across the Atlantic, and during the next few hundred years the population in the New World grew dramatically. From the eastern seaboard, they moved ever westward, building homes, breaking the soil, planting crops, founding settlements. The country was growing. All along the way the bison was a welcome source of free meat, there for the taking. In order to save or increase their limited numbers of livestock, the pioneers depended upon wild animals for food.

The bison that were killed to be eaten did not reduce the total population significantly, but in time the animals disappeared east of the Mississippi River. By the time the bison disappeared in the eastern United States, about 1800, the white man's domestic herds of livestock had grown sufficiently to become his main source of meat. The bison's disappearance in the East was an inevitable result of settlement of the land. Bison west of the Rocky Mountains were also killed for food by men exploring and moving into the region. The herds had been very small in that area anyway, and they, too, disappeared early, probably by 1840. But in the early 1800s, millions of bison still roamed the plains from Texas to Canada. They seemed to be in no danger of extinction.

Then, starting around 1830, white hunters began to kill bison, not for necessary food but merely for their hides or tongues, or simply for the satisfaction of seeing them die. Eventually, hunting became a political and military policy of our government, the purpose of which was to eliminate the animal that was all-important to the Indians. During the next fifty-five years the species was indeed all but exterminated.

Volumes have been written about those years of slaughter, but, in brief, the history of the bison's near-extermination is as follows:

1830: Systematic destruction began.

1840: The bison, never large in numbers west of the Rocky Mountains, disappeared from that area.

1848: Records of the American Fur Company show that they shipped 110,000 bison robes and 25,000 tongues that year. There were many such companies.

1860s: The railroads that were built across the Great Plains during this period divided the bison into two great herds, the southern and the northern. Many animals were killed to feed railway crews and army posts. The Indians, concerned over the destruction of the bison, made attacks on the trains or on the hunters. In 1864 the Idaho State Legislature passed the first law to protect the bison—but only after it was gone from the state.

1870: The trading of robes and tongues had become a major industry, and an estimated two million bison were killed that year on the southern plains. That same year a new menace appeared. Several bales of bison skins were shipped to Germany for tanning into fine leather by a newly discovered process. American tanners soon learned the process or developed a similar one.

By now, the gathering and shipping of bones had also become a big business. They were used in refining sugar and making fertilizer and fine bone china. Bison bones brought from $2.50 to $15 a ton. Based on an average price of $8 per ton, in Kansas alone, they brought $2.5 million between 1868 and 1881. On the assumption that about one hundred skeletons were required to make one ton of bones, this represented the slaughter of more than 31 million bison.

1871: This year marked the beginning of the end for the southern herd; the greatest slaughter took place along the railroads. One firm in St. Louis alone traded 250,000 hides that year.

Demand for bison skins for leather continued; one dealer sent circulars to the bison ranges offering good prices for hides taken any time of the year. Until then most of them had been used for robes; therefore bison had been killed only in winter, when the hair was long and fine. With the increased demand for hides, slaughter became a year-round activity and furthered the decline of the species even more.

Unfortunately for the bison, powerful breech-loading, long-range rifles such as the various big Sharps rifles were developed to near perfection at this time.

Some people in the West began to think about saving the bison, and Wyoming passed a law prohibiting the wasting of meat. Since such laws were not enforced, they did little to protect the animal. On March 13, 1871, a Mr. Richard C. McCormick of Arizona introduced a bill into the House of Representatives recommending a fine for the killing of a bison except for its hide or for food. The bill was never voted on.

1872: During this year—and the next two—an average of 5,000 bison were killed each day, every day of the year, as ten thousand hunters poured onto the plains. One railroad shipped over a million pounds of bison bones. Bison hunting became a popular sport for the rich. In the

At one time, collecting and selling bison bones was a profitable business.

midst of all this, treaties with the Indians were openly violated.

Another member of Congress proposed more legislation, but the effort was too feeble to succeed. And when Colorado managed to pass a law prohibiting the wasting of bison meat, it was not enforced. The Kansas legislature also passed a similar bill that same year, but the governor vetoed it.

1873: On the southern plains, slaughter reached its peak that year. One railroad shipped nearly three million pounds of bones. Hides sold for $1.25 each; tongues brought 25 cents apiece; most of the meat was left to rot. A railway engineer said it was possible to walk for "100 miles" along the Santa Fe Railroad's right-of-way by stepping from one bison carcass to another.

The United States Government continued to do nothing to save the species. Columbus Delano, Secretary of the Interior under President Grant, wrote in his 1873 report: "I would not seriously regret the total disappearance of the buffalo from our western prairies, in its effect upon the Indians. I would regard it rather as a means of hastening their sense of dependence upon the products of the soil and their own labors."

1874: This year marked the virtual end of the great southern herd. Auctions in Fort Worth, Texas, were moving 200,000 hides in a day or two. One railroad shipped nearly 7 million pounds of bones.

Congress came closer to helping the bison than it had before: both the House and the Senate passed a bill that protected the females and did away with wanton destruction. However, President Grant refused to sign the bill. Secretary Delano was quoted as saying that he would rejoice when the last bison was exterminated.

49

1875: Kansas and Colorado managed to pass laws protecting the bison, but there were none left in those states. A few remained in Texas, but when that state's legislature moved to protect the bison, General Phil Sheridan appeared before the assembly and suggested that every hunter be given a medal "with a dead buffalo on one side and a discouraged Indian on the other." He added that, once the animals were exterminated, the Indians would be controlled and civilization could advance.

1876: The hunters had been kept off the northern plains by treaties with the Indians, but with the elimination of the southern herd they had started moving north. The Northern Pacific Railroad, anxious to advance, ignored the treaties and sent in a survey party. The Indians killed some of the men, and General George Custer was sent to investigate. The massacre at the battle of the Little Big Horn in June is history. But the country was being opened, and the northern herd was next in line for destruction.

1877: A few bison were discovered in Texas and killed.

1880: For the first time, wholesale slaughter of the northern herd began. New Mexico passed a protective law, again after the bison were gone.

1881: The greatest slaughter of the northern herds took place during the winter of 1881–82. One dealer alone shipped more than 260,000 hides. One county in Montana shipped out 180,000 skins. Prices paid for "buffalo" robes ranged from $2.50 to $4.

1882: A reported five thousand hunters were on the range that year. The season of 1882–83 sealed the fate of the northern herd. Many hunters thought the bison had moved north into Canada but they had not. They had been eliminated. The Northern Pacific Railroad hauled nearly three times as many hides as the year before. During this period many bison were killed for their tongues only, with not a pound of meat or a hide touched. Hunters got 25 cents apiece for the tongues.

1883: By the middle of the year nearly all the bison were gone. In October a herd numbering between 1,000 and 1,200 was found in western Dakota, not far from the present town of Bison, South Dakota. They were slaughtered to the last animal. Elsewhere, hunters found no bison to shoot.

The Dakota Territorial Legislature enacted a protective law that year. The law was not enforced, but it hardly mattered: for all practical purposes, wild bison were gone.

1886: The Smithsonian Institution sent a party out West to obtain bison specimens for the U.S. National Museum. After much effort, a few were finally located near the LU Bar Ranch in Montana. Twenty-five of them were collected for taxidermic mounting and for scientific study.

C. J. Jones, commonly called "Buffalo Jones," captured thirteen calves in the southern range as a nucleus of a private herd.

1887: One last lot of robes sold in Texas for $10 per robe.

1889: The last four animals of the southern herd were killed in Texas. A report by William T. Hornaday listed a total of 256 bison in captivity, with another 200 in Yellowstone National Park. The 85 wild ones in the United States and about 550 wild ones in northern Canada brought the grand total of live bison in all North America to 1,091.

1893: The Canadian government made it unlawful to kill bison, but there was not much enforcement.

1894: There was still no Federal law protecting bison in the United States. A poacher who killed this animal in Yellowstone National Park suffered only the slight penalty of having his outfit confiscated and being expelled from the park. Poaching had almost exterminated the Yellowstone herd. With taxidermists paying high prices for bison, now a very rare animal, temptation had been too great to resist. After all, a New York millionaire had been willing to pay $1,500 for a mounted head.

The first real effort made by the United States to save the bison came in May of 1894, when Congress passed a law making it unlawful to hunt bison in Yellowstone National Park. Conviction carried a $1,000 fine or imprisonment. However, that same year the few wild ones that were discovered in the Rocky Mountains of Colorado were killed.

1897: The Northwest Mounted Police of Canada began patrolling the bison range in the north, thus giving the herd a chance to grow. In the United States, what is believed to be the last four wild bison in the entire country were killed in Colorado, near Bison Peak.

1900: The number of bison in North America hit an all-time low: the only wild ones—fewer than 300—were in Canada; the total population of living bison was set at 541.

After 1900: Canada posted resident game wardens in the north in 1911 to protect the bison; most of the area was made into Wood Buffalo National Park in 1922. In the United States, Congress still was not doing much, but it made little difference since there were none to protect. A few remained in Yellowstone National Park, a few in private herds—that was all.

Congress finally appropriated money to buy bison from private herds to restock the depleted herd in Yellowstone Park. The National Bison Society was formed to lend aid to the nearly extinct species and, along with the New York Zoological Society, advocated establishing herds that would be under Federal protection. Within a few years some national refuges were created. In 1907 the New York Zoological Society made a gift of 15 animals to form the nucleus of a herd at the Wichita Mountains National Wildlife Refuge in Oklahoma. In 1908 another 34 bison were donated by the National Bison Society to develop a herd at the National Bison Range in Montana. In 1913 a private citizen, J. W. Gilbert of Nebraska, gave the American people a small number of bison that started the herd now living on the Fort Niobrara Refuge in Nebraska. The city of Portland, Oregon, gave 6 animals to the Sullys Hill National Game Preserve in North Dakota.

Slowly, bison purchased from private herds and placed in big-game sanctuaries multiplied and saved the species from extinction. By 1912 the United States had 2,000 bison; by 1926 there were more than 4,000; in Canada there were 12,000. In 1943 there were 6,000 in the United

States. Today, bison in the United States and Canada number over 30,000.

What really caused the bison, the largest land animal in North America, to almost vanish? Was it the railroads, the mighty buffalo guns, the callousness and greed of man, official government and military policy, the animal's inability to outwit man?

Certainly the railroads made it much easier for the hunters to get to the bison herds and for the sellers to ship the hides, tongues, and bones to market. The iron rails that brought in settlers opened up the Great Plains and also helped create Indian troubles.

The powerful buffalo guns were the main instrument of destruction, and their near-perfection coincided with the beginning of the end for the bison. They often weighed more than 20 pounds and, with their long-range accuracy, were devastating. The big Sharps 50-120-550 fired a slug of lead 2 inches long and $\frac{1}{2}$ inch in diameter, weighing eight to the pound. The Indians said of these rifles that they "shoot today and kill tomorrow." Such nicknames as "big fifty," "Old Reliable," and "old poison slinger" were well earned. With such a weapon it was possible for a skilled hunter to kill over 100 bison without moving from one spot. He could kill 250 in one day, 3,000 in one month, 5,700 a year, and perhaps 30,000 in a lifetime.

Man's callousness and greed of course cannot be overlooked. Thousands of bison were killed for "sport," slain by men who shot them from moving trains, who did not care whether the animals were crippled or not, and who left the dead, untouched, to rot on the prairies. There was easy money in shooting bison, and expert riflemen could make thousands of dollars hunting them down. If only the tongues were taken, at 25 cents each, a daily kill of 100 bison would bring $25. Greed and lack of feeling certainly contributed to the wholesale slaughter of the species.

It is a sad truth that the government and the military used the extermination of the bison as a means of subduing the Indians. President Grant

A Sharps Old Reliable Sporting Rifle, an 1874 model.

refused to sign a bill that would have protected many of the bison that were still left. As General Sheridan said, in reference to the hunters:

These men have done in the last two years, and will do in the next year, more to settle the vexed Indian question than the entire regular army has done in the last 30 years. They are destroying the Indian's commissary; and it is a well known fact that an army losing its base of supplies is placed at a great disadvantage. Send them powder and lead, if you will; but, for the sake of lasting peace, let them kill, skin, and sell until the buffaloes are exterminated. Then your prairies can be covered with speckled cattle and the festive cowboy, who follows the hunter as a second forerunner of an advanced civilization.

Much has been said about the bison's unadaptability; many claim that if the animal had been wary and alert, it would have learned to cope with man and his rifle and would have survived in great numbers. But the bison had never had any serious enemies. If the wolf and the grizzly could not harm it to any great extent, why should it have feared the little animal that walked awkwardly on its hind legs? And, realistically, what measures could the bison have taken to prevent its own destruction?

All of these things add up to the real reason why the animal was eliminated: civilization.

If the bison had not been wiped out in the 1880s, it would have only been a matter of years before the westward movement of men accomplished the same thing. They could not possibly have lived in close association with large herds of wild bison. Such animals did not mix well with crops and farmlands, with domestic stock and fences, with a growing human population and developing settlements. What fence could be easily built that would stop a bison bull intent on passing that way? And what effect would a passing herd of a million bison have on a wheat field just before harvest time? Furthermore, the animal's lack of fear, which made it vulnerable to guns, also made it dangerous to cattle, horses, or any person who happened to get in its way.

The bison, born a wilderness animal, could not survive in vast numbers

55

in a rapidly expanding country, but there are still thousands of them in North America. They go about their daily and seasonal lives much as they have for centuries, and anyone can visit a refuge or park, or perhaps a private herd, and watch, photograph, and enjoy them.

I have often been asked about the equipment I use to photograph wild-life. I have worked up a basic outfit which consists of two Nikon F, 35-mm single-lens reflex camera bodies, an electric motor drive for one camera, and a group of high-quality lenses with focal lengths of 58 mm, 135 mm, 200 mm, 300 mm, 400 mm and 640 mm. The lenses are of different makes, though most of them are Auto-Nikkor. I use a heavy wooden tripod with the long lenses and whenever convenient with the shorter ones. The filters I use most often for black and white films are light yellow, orange, red, and green. My light meters are the Weston Master V and the Norwood Super Director. I use Kodak's Panatomic-X and Tri-X film, and in order to obtain the highest possible quality I

process all my own black and white film and make my own prints.

Other useful accessories that travel with me include a self-timer so that I can appear in some of the photographs, a cable release for smooth operation of the shutter when I'm using long lenses, extension tubes for close work, flash equipment for night work, and remote-control equipment, which I use when close approach to the subject or telephoto photography is not feasible.

Regardless of whether you take along a camera or not, a trip to bison country is worthwhile. Perhaps, as I have done, you will conjure up visions of countless shaggy creatures thundering across the great North American plains, making the very ground quake at their passing.

Spring

THE YEARLING bison calf looks up, alert to a sound it has never heard before. From out on the flat, the source unseen in the gloom of early dawn, comes a series of *plops!* in a repeated pattern. Morning light comes slowly, but eventually the youngster can see well enough to inspect its surroundings and discover who or what is producing such a strange noise. Surely it cannot come from that group of large birds, strutting and dancing a short distance away? But yes, those birds *are* making that plopping sound, which punctuates their dance steps. Actually, only the males do so, by rapidly inflating and deflating large sacs on their necks—but the calf does not know this. Nor does it know that these are sage grouse, largest of the grouse tribe, performing their spectacular mating dance.

Baby great horned owls.

And what a sight it is to watch the handsome males, holding their tails stiffly fanned out, show off in front of the seemingly unmoved females.

It is spring, and though snows still chill many parts of the bison's vast range, each day brings new signs that winter is over. The earliest nesting birds, such as the great horned owls, are already watching over their young in the nest, shielding them from the cold and the occasional snow flurries by covering them with their soft, thick feathers.

As the days grow longer and the warmth increases, new grass, green and succulent, stirs the bison herd to greater activity; it moves as if in response to some unseen, age-old force.

Much has been written about the migrations of bison, and many debates still remain unsettled. Early observers believed that the herds traveled great distances—to the southern plains and even into Mexico for the winter, and back to the Dakotas, Montana, and Canada for the summer months. But such journeys would have involved enormous distances, and later observers began to question this migratory pattern.

59

Although the bison seemed to be always in motion, slowly, restlessly moving to new pastures, this movement began to be accepted not as true migration but more or less as wandering, because they were often seen heading north in the fall or south in the spring.

Bison did tend to leave the southernmost part of the southern range—Mexico and Texas—to escape summer's intense heat, but other than that they seemed to move at random. An animal as well prepared for winter's worst as the bison did not need to fear the change of seasons. It could take care of itself in the bitterest cold weather and had problems only with the deepest snows.

A moving herd does not remain in one compact group, shoulder to shoulder. It travels in many loosely knit bands of animals numbering from a few to several score. These groups mingle, drift apart, form new groups, and separate again, apparently maintaining some relationship yet rarely crowding one another. Even when the bison numbered in the millions, there was room for all of them on the range.

Frank G. Roe probably summed up the bison's movements as well as anyone by saying that "these wanderings were utterly erratic and unpredictable and might occur regardless of time, place, or season, with any number, in any direction, in any manner, under any conditions, and for any reason—which is to say, for no 'reason' at all."

Herds today, such as those in Wood Buffalo National Park and Yellowstone National Park, tend to move seasonally only very short distances, or even not at all.

Especially in Wood Buffalo Park, which is not enclosed by fences, the movements of bison herds can be thoroughly studied. The animals do not seem to mind the severe winter temperatures that are typical of that region. In his *History, Range, and Home Life of the Northern Bison,* J. Dewey Soper related their seasonal movements in detail. Motivation, he observed, seems to be solely due to the need for a new food supply; their movements bear no relation to climate, elevation, or compass direction. In fact, they head mostly eastward—not southward—in the fall. To get

Bison travel in loosely knit bands, their movements erratic.

to their main wintering areas, some herds have covered airline distances of from 20 to more than 100 miles. Others have traveled only 5 to 10 miles; none have gone more than 150.

Movement for such short distances can hardly be termed migration in the usual sense, and it is now generally accepted that bison did not, and do not, make long semiannual migrations.

Whether bison migrate or not may be debatable, but there is one thing about these animals that we do know: they itch! And they (like people) consider uninhibited scratching one of life's great pleasures. Every observer of bison knows that they love to scratch, and in the spring this urge is greatest. The long, dense winter coat is loosening and the old hair coming off in patches, giving the bison a ragged, tattered look and making it itch all over. The need to scratch is overwhelming, and any object that helps relieve the itching will do. Its hind feet are used most often, but it will also rub against rocks until they are worn smooth, or against trees until the bark is worn off, or—after civilization moved far enough west—against telegraph poles, which bison discovered to be ideal scratching posts. Many a pole was flattened by a large bull rubbing against it a bit too vigorously. Even the large spikes that were imbedded in the replaced poles did not deter them. Indeed, these metal protuberances proved to be even better for scratching. Cabins, wagons, fences—all have been reported severely damaged.

By the time the winter coat is rubbed away, a new annoyance has

Insects—a springtime nuisance.

arrived: springtime's crop of insects. Wallowing in mud or dust seems to protect bison against insects and to relieve itching. Although summer is the peak season for wallowing, the bison does a lot of it in the spring (or any time it feels an itch, regardless of the season).

Bulls, especially mature ones, seem to wallow much more than cows. They stretch out, rub their heads vigorously back and forth on the ground, and kick the dust or mud up with their feet. They also try to roll

63

Wallowing relieves itching and helps bison ward off insects.

over onto their backs, but the high hump on the shoulders prevents them from doing so. After one side is thoroughly dusted or coated with mud, they go through the same routine on the other side. The job completed, they stand up and shake the dust off in great clouds. The plastering of mud or dust that remains helps ward off the annoying insects.

A typical buffalo wallow is a saucer-shaped depression in the ground, possibly a foot or so deep and eight to ten or more feet in diameter. Constant use keeps the area completely bare of any plant life. There are thousands of these wallows on the bison's summer ranges.

Some of the greatest fatalities among bison herds have occurred in the spring, when ice begins to break up on the lakes and waterways and rivers run too full, overflowing their banks and turning land only recently frozen solid into treacherous bogs. Habit can be a deadly thing: all winter bison can safely cross certain lakes and rivers on thick ice. But in the spring that same ice gets thinner and weaker, and its breaking up is sometimes helped along by the added weight of hundreds of bison. When this happens, losses can be great. Historians report that many of our larger rivers in the Great Plains have been lined with the rotting carcasses of bison that drowned when spring ice gave way. The bison is a strong

A typical wallow, in Elk Island National Park, Alberta, Canada.

swimmer, but if one falls through weak ice, it is usually the end, for a hoofed animal is not equipped to grasp or hold. It can do nothing but flounder in the cold water until it is too exhausted to keep afloat.

Wood Buffalo National Park Superintendent Ed Olson wrote me that the total park loss from drowning runs around one hundred a year, mostly in the spring and mostly in the Peace River. William A. Fuller has stated that twenty to fifty bison are usually reported drowned in that river during the ice breakup.

When not handicapped by ice, the bison swims without hesitation, readily crossing large rivers or lakes. It rides low in the water, with usually only the upper part of its head above the surface. But bison are sometimes caught in spring floods, as J. Dewey Soper reported from Wood Buffalo National Park. In such areas as the Peace–Athabasca River delta, rivers rise with abnormal rapidity, and animals trapped in the lower areas by the flood may not be able to reach higher ground in time. William A. Fuller noted losses of about five hundred animals in the delta in the spring of 1958; as many as three thousand bison were lost in 1960 when the entire shore line of Lake Claire was inundated. Ed Olson stated that over eighteen hundred drownings occurred in the spring of 1959—this was only one of four serious floodings that have occurred since 1957.

With the spring thaws, once-frozen bog holes pose a threat to bison, though most authorities do not believe that they are a major hazard.

This season is not, however, all danger and discomfort. In response to the warm sun, new grasses flourish and the bison, enjoying a richer diet, begins to put on weight. On the Great Plains many kinds of nutritious grasses cover the rolling hills, level prairies, and creek bottoms, making this vast central region of North America an ideal range. The eastern portion was known as the tall-grass prairie; the central, the mid-grass prairie; the western, the short-grass plains. These are not areas sharply delineated by boundaries, but places where the dominant grasses are

The grassy rolling hills of Custer State Park make an ideal habitat.

determined by soil and moisture conditions.

The tall-grass prairie, typified by relatively heavy rainfall, has the most luxuriant grass growth. It extends from the southern parts of the Canadian provinces of Alberta, Saskatchewan, and Manitoba south through the eastern parts of the Dakotas, Nebraska, and Kansas and the western portions of Minnesota and Iowa into Oklahoma. Dense stands of tall bluestem grass, often growing as high as eight feet, share the land with slightly shorter species, such as switch grass and Indian grass.

Just to the west of the tall-grass prairie is a region of slightly less rainfall. It forms a band which extends roughly from southern Saskatchewan down through the Dakotas, Nebraska, Kansas, Oklahoma, and into Texas. This vast area is characterized by grasses from two to four feet high, the most important or dominant of them being little bluestem grass, but including needle grass, June grass, western wheat grass, and others.

67

Farther westward is a still drier area, the semi-arid short-grass plains, which extends from southern Alberta and Saskatchewan south through eastern Montana, Wyoming, and Colorado; touches western portions of the Dakotas, Nebraska, Kansas, and Oklahoma; and continues into Texas, New Mexico, and Arizona. Buffalo grass and blue grama grasses dominate in this sweeping stretch of land, for they are able to flourish with little moisture. These species actually spread during the dust-bowl days of the 1930s, replacing less drought-resistant grasses.

Wood bison occupy a habitat in the northern part of Canada that is different from the one most of us have learned to associate with the bison. There, in what is now Wood Buffalo National Park, the bison live amid heavy stands of timber, wandering among spruce, aspen, and poplar trees that grow up to two feet in diameter. It is nerve-racking to a wild-life photographer rambling along a trail through thick willow or aspen thickets suddenly to meet a very solid-looking bull that clearly has no intention of yielding the right of way.

This area also has immense tracts of open land with parklike stands of pine, barren and rocky hills, open muskegs, low flood plains, and delta marshes—all interspersed with upland meadows and plains. During the warm months the wood bison seem to prefer a region combining pure stands of aspen or balsam poplar with richly carpeted upland prairies.

The more important of these forage grasses include the wheat grasses, broom grasses, wild rye, vanilla grass, June grass, meadow grasses, and feather grass. In addition, the herds munch on vetch and pea vine.

Spring brings new life to the bison herds. After a gestation period of nine or nine and a half months, calves are born, mostly during late April, May, and even June. However, records show that bison cows give birth during every month of the year.

At Nebraska's Fort Niobrara Refuge, for example, a calf was born in 1966 on March 26; in 1967 one was born on November 19. These two

The sun-dappled shade of a forest in Wood Buffalo National Park.

birth dates are the earliest and latest recorded at this refuge. In 1967, Custer State Park in South Dakota reported a birth on December 2; at the Wichita Mountains National Wildlife Refuge in Oklahoma a calf was born in mid-December of that same year.

Twin births are rare. In the 1930s, a cow and two newborn calves

69

were found dead together at the National Bison Range, and it is assumed that the calves were twins. Another case was reported from the same refuge in 1967. Frank G. Roe says in his book, *The North American Buffalo,* "I have consulted the annual reports from the various buffalo parks (Wood Buffalo Park, Northwest Territories, Wainwright Buffalo Park, and Elk Island, Alberta) from their inception until the closing of Wainwright Park (1904–40), but have found no mention of twin calves in any of them."

When the cow bison feels her calf is about to be born, she tends to move off from the main herd, often seeking a slightly secluded spot such as a ravine or an area of tall grasses. There a 30- to 70-pound calf is born and is licked clean by its mother.

The number of males born apparently holds only a slight edge over the number of females. William A. Fuller examined the fetuses from 472 cows killed during herd-reduction operations in Wood Buffalo National Park from 1952 to 1956 and noted that 53 per cent were males. In the 1916 *Annual Report of the American Bison Society,* T. S. Palmer noted that, in a study of 460 bison, 54 per cent of the young were male.

In striking contrast to the chocolate brown and black color of adult bison, a newly born calf is a bright yellowish red. Since the hump is not pronounced at birth, the baby bears a close resemblance to a calf of domestic cattle. It is born with its eyes open and is able to stand, though

A young bison follows its mother around for the first year.

somewhat shakily, for its first meal. The mother's milk is not plentiful, but it is exceedingly rich and gives the baby a good nutritious start in life.

It takes only a few days for the young calf to become strong enough to keep up with the herd, and from then on it is a wanderer, typical of its kind. It follows its mother around until the following spring, when it must yield its position to a new brother or sister.

The calves' mothers and other adult bison in the herd do an admirable job of protecting the newborn. Few animals in search of a meal are willing to brave those deadly horns. Predators are opportunists: they take what they can get—whatever comes easiest. And so rapidly do the babies gain strength that after just a few days even a lone calf is more than any but the largest, most determined animals care to tackle. Thus, at peace with the world, the bison herds nibble the greening grasses as spring warms into summer.

71

Summer

IN JUNE, the world of the bison teems with activity. Before long the calves, which have grown noticeably, will be completely weaned and will join their elders in the pleasant pastime of grazing. The youngsters are becoming more independent with each passing day.

Other young wildlife species, themselves now able to explore the world around them, are also beginning to enjoy their freedom. An exploring wolf pup sniffs the ground outside the den. A young bobcat, on the prowl along a riverbank, discovers a recently dead fish and carries it around for hours. A dainty spotted mule deer fawn pauses in the dappled shade of the deep woods; somewhere nearby, the yellow-bellied marmot pokes its nose over the top of a rock, a good lookout point from which to scan the neighborhood for food—or foe.

Young great horned owls are growing fat on mice and gophers, while

By summer, the young bison has been weaned and is beginning to graze with the rest of the herd.

A wolf pup and a mule deer fawn explore the world of summertime.

A young bobcat learning to hunt for food. A cautious yellow-bellied marmot scans the neighborhood for a meal.

Young great horned owls have become more independent by summer.

the young of other species are still completely dependent on their parents. The mountain bluebird, for example, is kept busy hunting for food to feed its babies.

As summer progresses, bison calves continue to show signs of growing up. The reddish coat of babyhood is gradually being replaced by darker shaggy fur. By the time a bull calf is about two months old, his horns begin to show—mere stubs of the massive ones he carries as an adult. The hump on his back is a little more noticeable, too. Female calves start showing their horns a little later than the bulls do.

The warming of passions is coincident with the warming of the season, for summer is the rutting, or breeding, season for bison. This period seems to extend from June through September, but most of the breeding takes place during July and August. In northern climates, it begins somewhat

75

During the mating season, bulls tend to horn bushes, push one another around . . .

later—early August—and is of shorter duration than in the more southern regions. Some breeding does take place all year long.

In early summer, with little else to do on long, balmy days other than munch on succulent grasses, bison are healthy and fairly placid. But with the onset of the breeding season, the whole mood of the animals changes: the slow, lazy, almost slothful bison suddenly become belligerent, unpredictable, dangerous.

The entire herd displays restlessness, feeding periods are frequently interrupted, and the small bands in which bison move during most of the year join together. Normally aloof, the bulls now tend to push one another around a lot, sniff at the cows, bellow often, wallow much more frequently than seems necessary, repeatedly horn the ground or trees and bushes, and in general act aggressive with or without cause. This is *not* the time to approach too closely.

Only a very few one-year-old bulls are considered capable of breeding. Quite a few reach sexual maturity at the age of two; most are mature by

. . . and bellow a lot more than usual.

the time they reach their third birthday. These youngsters, however, do little breeding in the wild. They have to fight for the right to do so because the dominant older males—bulls from four to eight years old—do not willingly give up that hard-earned privilege.

Bison cows also demonstrate a similar pattern of sexual maturity. A small number of them breed as yearlings and give birth when they are two. A few more breed for the first time at the age of two, but most begin breeding during the third year, and bear a calf every year thereafter until they are twenty or older.

From records kept on wildlife refuges, where the ages of animals are known, we have learned a great deal about breeding ages. Information from Julian A. Howard, Refuge Manager of the Wichita Mountains Wildlife Refuge near Cache, Oklahoma, showed that an occasional yearling heifer will breed and then calve as a two-year-old. The oldest cow to bear a calf at this refuge was twenty-one years old. Robert C. Fields of the Fort Niobrara Refuge noted that a yearling heifer does breed once in a while. It is most apt to happen to a cow that is born early in the year and then bred late in the breeding season of that year. A twenty-year-old cow was the oldest to calve at Fort Niobrara. Assistant Superintendent Wes Broer of Custer State Park has also agreed that yearlings sometimes breed. There, the oldest cow to have a calf was sixteen years old. While thirty is considered very old for bison, an occasional one will reach forty. Interestingly, a private ranch in Wyoming reported that a thirty-eight-year-old cow gave birth.

As the rutting season approaches, the bulls travel about looking for cows unattended by a male. Sometimes, one bull manages to keep a small group of cows to himself. Other times he cannot drive off all bachelor bulls and so must share the cows. It is not unusual to have a third bull sneak in and steal a cow while two bulls are fighting.

Herd bulls are often challenged by lusty younger males eager to take part in breeding and willing to test their strength in combat. Even though these youngsters usually take a beating at first, one of them eventually proves his superiority by winning a fight and driving the older, established bull away. These leadership fights serve a function important to all species: perpetuation of the strong and the vigorous.

I once watched a lone bull in Wood Buffalo National Park exhibit typical rutting season behavior. He was definitely in an aggressive mood as he walked along the border of the timber; now and then he would hook a small tree or bush with a horn, easily breaking it or stripping the limbs off. Periodically he would tip his head up and bellow as he went, moving faster than the normal lazy gait of the bison.

At one point he paused at a recently used wallow, sniffed the ground a few seconds, urinated on the spot, and then proceeded to kneel and rub his head and horns in the damp area. Standing upright again, he let out a loud bellow and looked in my direction, seemingly just discovering my presence. His tail went up—a danger sign—and he turned toward me.

This wood bison was in an aggressive mood, so I quickly left.

This veteran of numerous battles was not friendly either.

The stare I got, and his general attitude, told me I had pushed my luck far enough. He left no doubt about it when he took a couple of steps toward me and hooked a small aspen with frightening quickness. I left.

On another occasion a huge bull immediately headed my way at a determined trot as soon.as he spied me, and I scrambled for cover in a nearby stand of large, closely spaced aspen trees. He went on, looking for a more worthy opponent.

When one bull approaches another bull at this time, chances are good that the challenger will not back down readily. He has come to fight, if need be, in an effort to steal a cow or two.

When a dominant bull faces a challenger, a ritual seemingly determines the actions of both animals. First the dominant bull stands and gives the challenger a hard look. This bellicose stare was enough to make me quit the field in haste, but it does not necessarily scare another bison bull.

If the challenger is not intimidated, the bull then begins to shake his head, as if reminding his opponent that he has horns and knows what to do with them, much as a boxer shadow-boxes or a wrestler flexes his muscles. The next step is snorting and pawing the ground, and possibly a certain amount of wallowing. Often some of these prelim-

Horn-to-horn combat. One spectator refused to leave his ringside seat.

inaries are omitted, and sometimes the challenging male does not wait around to see if the defender really means what he says.

If these bluffs fail to work, the bulls advance toward each other with heads lowered and tails erect. Once they butt heads, there begins an all-out shoving match, brute strength pitted against brute strength. Repeated attempts to hook with the wicked horns add to the fierceness of the contest. The almost gentle beginning can erupt into a series of violent charges, amazingly quick footwork, and a fantastic display of physical power. Most fights are short, with one bull quickly proving his mastery over the other. But clashes between well-matched bulls can go on until finally one or the other weakens. Injuries are not uncommon, but battles are seldom to the death. The heavy hair growth on the head and front portions of the body undoubtedly acts as padding and prevents more serious injuries.

The few fights I was able to observe in Wood Buffalo National Park were all of short duration. The dust the animals kicked up during these struggles obscured many details and when I tried to draw closer for a better view they wheeled away and trotted off into the brush. None of the bulls I saw fighting appeared to suffer injuries.

A dominant bull generally reigns for only a few years, and, once defeated, he is said never to attempt a comeback. Thenceforth he is a solitary individual, shunning close association with either sex. He often wanders off by himself to brood away his life in sullen isolation.

These old loners are in many respects the most dangerous wild animals in North America. If they have a mind to, they will stand in a trail and refuse to move for anything or anybody. Those I met while wandering in Wood Buffalo National Park were given a wide berth, for they are notoriously ill tempered and morose and have put more than one person to flight. Some of these old bulls live for many, many years, for they are practically immune to predation, being too tough for man to eat or predators to kill.

Actual breeding takes place whenever a cow is ready. A bull sniffs

While tending a cow, a bull often places his head on her back.

the cows constantly to find one that is sufficiently in heat for him to begin a period of tending. During this period, which can last hours or even days, the bull and cow lick each other's fur, butt heads gently, and stay close to one another. The bull often places his head on the cow's back. When the cow is ready, mating takes place. Cows are polyestrous, so mating may take place several times during the rutting season.

Bison do not spend all their time in summer fighting and breeding, however, and except for the breeding bulls they prosper and grow fat. Descriptive words such as huge are often misused, but in the case of this animal, the adjective is correct. The largest bulls weighed have tipped the scales at nearly 3,000 pounds, while those weighing over a ton are not uncommon.

Wood Buffalo National Park Superintendent Ed Olson has personally seen one that weighed 2,634 pounds. But, he hastened to add, that

83

animal was past its prime. It was lean when weighed and had probably reached about 3,000 pounds in its best days.

Average weights give a better idea of the animal's normal size than maximum figures do. At the National Bison Range at Moiese, Montana, during a recent nine-year period, weights of one hundred and twenty-five bulls, five years and older, were recorded. The lightest was 1,224 pounds; the heaviest, 1,980 pounds. The average weight was 1,678 pounds. However, these bulls were weighed in October, during the Refuge's annual roundup, and they were not at their heaviest following the rutting period. At the same time, one hundred and sixty cows, also five or more years old, were weighed. The lightest was 695 pounds while the heaviest was 1,075 pounds; the average weight: 985 pounds.

Similar information from the Wichita Mountains Refuge in Oklahoma gives the average weight of fifty-five bulls, age five and up, as 1,333 pounds, with extremes of 860 and 1,795 pounds. These figures do not represent maximum weights, since they were obtained in the fall. Seventy-nine cows of the same age group averaged 861 pounds, with a low and a high of 735 and 1,075 pounds respectively.

At Fort Niobrara Refuge in Nebraska, bulls of five or more years averaged 1,813 pounds, with 1,580-pound and 2,000-pound extremes. Forty-two cows in the same age group averaged 1,085 pounds, with a 890-pound low and a 1,370-pound high.

A rutting bull that spends most of his time challenging and fighting other bulls or chasing cows spends less time eating. Again, the managed herds on our wildlife refuges provide data on the extent of weight loss during the breeding season.

Refuge Manager Joe Mazzoni of the National Bison Range supplied figures from a study made in 1963 in which six bulls were weighed before and after the rutting season. They were all in the four-to seven-year age group. When first weighed on July 17, the animals were from 1,545 to 1,950 pounds. When weighed on October 8, each bull had lost from 120 to 260 pounds, the average loss being 223 pounds. Therefore

After their morning feeding, bison take life easy.

bulls weighing 1,800 pounds or more in October probably exceeded 2,000 pounds before the rut.

Robert C. Fields provided similar information from the Fort Niobrara Refuge. When eight bulls five to ten years of age were weighed in June, 1966, they ranged from 1,700 to 2,250 pounds. In October, their losses were between 150 and 380 pounds. When some of these same animals were then weighed the following July, each bull had gained back weight approximately equal to, or even greater than, the pre-rut weight of 1966.

A typical summer day for a bison herd begins at first light. After spending the dark hours resting, they are astir early and start to feed while the prairies are still wet with dew. They continue feeding in a leisurely fashion until late morning, by which time their appetites seem satisfied. By then the sun is high, the day warmer, and the animals are ready to bask in the sunshine, chew a cud for hours, and take life easy.

Some of them seek the shade of a tree, but bison in general do not seem to mind the sunlight. They are little inclined to do much more than nap, wallow, scratch, and visit a salt lick. An unhurried trip to the nearest water hole sometimes breaks the monotony of the long afternoon.

Bison need water and will often travel many miles to find it, but they are able to do without it for much longer periods than our domestic cattle and therefore can live in some of the continent's drier regions.

By late afternoon the languid mood passes and the herd rouses itself. Obviously intent upon ending the day with a full rumen, the animals begin feeding again and by sundown are ready to find a place to spend the night.

This daily summer pattern is often interrupted for a number of reasons. In addition to the fact that it is the rutting season, bison must

A small band of bison visit a creek for a leisurely drink.

deal with insect pests, fires, drought, tornadoes, thunderstorms, predators that harass the herd, and other annoyances.

Insect pests are at their worst in early summer. Vexed by their unremitting attacks, bison seek relief by wallowing, standing in a breeze, and frequently swishing their too-short tails. Ignoring these efforts, the winged tormentor persevere, swarming about the animals from head to flanks and burrowing into the long hair.

It has often been said that the main deterrent to the advance of civilization in the north is the presence of biting and stinging insects. Anyone who has spent much time in Alaska or northern Canada in early summer will not disagree with this statement. I am sure that a person without some form of protection would soon be driven insane by their constant assaults.

Wood bison are confronted with a disconcerting assortment of insect pests, including mosquitoes, black flies, deer flies, sand flies, and the vicious "bulldog" fly. The mosquitoes are at their worst from early June until early August. The bulldog is most vicious during the hottest days of July and August. This fly, of the genus *Tabanus,* is probably the northern bison's greatest scourge. It is distressing to watch an animal in such great discomfort, flicking its tail, stamping its feet, shaking its head, while the insects continue to pester it. Many times I have been thankful for protective clothing, my head net, and modern insect repellents.

The barbed seeds of various plants also add to the bison's discomfort because they get into the dense hair and can irritate the animal's sensitive skin if they come into contact with it. Squirreltail grass and spear grass are two of the offenders; both have seeds with barbed awns that cling to hair and eventually work their way through to the skin, causing sores. Interestingly, Ernest Thompson Seton noted that many old bison wallows on the Great Plains were rimmed with an unusually heavy growth of spear grass. It is assumed the grass got its start from seeds the bison dislodged while wallowing.

In early summer there is no escaping that winged tormentor, the fly.

Summer

The latter part of summer is more pleasant for the bison. Forage is plentiful, the rutting season is over—or about to end—the insect pests are gone, and the weather is comfortable. There are a few problems, but most of them are not important.

Lack of water, however, can be serious. Drought undoubtedly has caused great discomfort to the bison at various times in its history. Especially in the desert Southwest, water can become a critical item in dry years, and this could be a strong determining factor in the bison's moves away from the plains of Texas and other areas in the summer.

The tornado, a fearful show of nature's strength, is a phenomenon against which the bison has no defense. Historians tell us that the dark funnel clouds caused the herds to stampede in terror, and Mari Sandoz in *The Buffalo Hunters* related a story the Sioux Indians still tell of a long cloud that dipped down into a panic-stricken herd and killed hundreds of the animals.

On investigation after the storm, Miss Sandoz wrote, the Indians found the bison "in a long rick, as though lifted and sown along for a quarter of a mile, several deep, sometimes four, five on top of each other, broken and twisted, some stripped of their hair, some with the eyes hanging down their faces, drawn out of their skulls. Mixed in with the buffaloes were big loose clumps of hairs, weeds, grass, and splintered wood."

Lightning also has reputedly caused many bison stampedes. Again, the power of nature is an awesome thing. Just as sheep and cattle are sometimes killed today, many bison in the past were killed by violent electric storms that sweep the Great Plains every summer.

Prairie fires are frightening. In late summer, when the grass becomes crisp and dry, it takes only a small spark to unleash a holocaust. Lightning probably furnishes some of the sparks, and in the tall-grass prairies, where the grasses are high and dense, such a fire can reach fantastic proportions. The writings of earlier historians are liberally sprinkled with graphic accounts of these fires and their effect on wild-

89

A bison bull and a pickup truck debating the right of way. (P.S. The bull yielded.)

life. Whole herds of bison had their hair singed off; many were blinded by fire; incredible numbers were maimed, scorched, and roasted. In sum, the ground would be littered with dead and dying bison in the wake of a prairie fire.

In recent years a new hazard has appeared which has meant death to many species of wildlife in North America—the motor vehicle. In most areas in which we now find bison, the car or truck is not of major importance. Highways stretch across the open plains, allowing both man and beast good visibility, and usually the vehicles are not moving very rapidly. Yet bison have been killed on highways. William A. Fuller wrote in his 1966 report on the bison of Wood Buffalo National Park:

The first, and so far only, victim of the machine age was a bull that lost an encounter with a truck on the night of August 27, 1951. The driver's account of the incident is not very clear, but it seems he failed to see the animal by the light of his headlights. The bison sustained a broken neck and the truck a broken radiator.

I can understand why the truck driver's account was "not very clear," for in September, 1967, I myself had an encounter with a small bison herd while driving at night in the same park, and I'll admit things happened too quickly for me to take notes. A friend of mine and I, in

90

separate vehicles, were driving back to Fort Smith, Northwest Territories, from Pine Lake. I was leading in my Volkswagen sedan; Don Jenkins, of Fort Smith, was following in his pickup truck. I had seen many bison in recent days and was driving cautiously to avoid hitting any animal in the dark. My speed was about 40 miles an hour. Suddenly, all I could see just beyond the windshield was dark hair. Severe jolts made me nearly lose control of the car, but I managed to hold it on the road and stopped. I was shaken but unhurt.

On investigation I discovered that the left headlight was gone and there were dents in the hood, the right front fender, the right door and panel in back of the right door, and the right rear fender. We had been rounding a curve to our left, so that Don's headlights were shining off to the right of the road, and he was able to tell me what had happened. From our right, a small herd had come out of the heavy aspen timber at a full run and on a collision course with my car. The lead bison, passing in front of me (the hair I saw through the windshield), had been hit by my left front fender. My headlight had been knocked out and the animal had been bowled over, but it got up and ran off, apparently unhurt.

The second bison braked to a stop and reared up, allowing the little car to pass under its forequarters. This animal probably made all the dents on the right side of the car. The rest of the herd passed between my car and the truck, and to Don it looked as if I had been engulfed by the animals. Thoroughly alarmed, he stopped and ran forward, fully expecting to find the Volkswagen reduced to rubble. We both marveled at the small amount of damage to the car, which would have been much greater had any of the bison hit it squarely.

The driver of a large trailer truck that struck a big bull one night a couple weeks earlier could testify to the effect that an impact with such a hulking animal has. He hit it very solidly while traveling quite fast on a straight stretch of road. The bull was killed outright and the front end of that heavy truck was completely smashed in. A wrecker was needed to move it away.

During the few weeks I was in the area, I heard of at least four bison that met a similar fate, including two that were killed by a pickup driven by a park employee.

Despite the various problems and fatalities that can occur in any given locality, the bison herds flourish in the summer, and when fall comes they are in prime condition.

Autumn

WITH THE ARRIVAL of September comes a change, ever so slight at first, that ushers in a new season. The first sign is a nip in the night air, even though the days are still warm. In many parts of North America, autumn is the finest time of year. Golden days offset the chilly nights, making it possible to postpone thoughts of winter's icy blasts. Why dwell on that prospect when there are many weeks of wonderful weather for all to enjoy?

The bison are well padded with fat from the plentiful and easily obtained foods of summer and will soon be covered with a heavy blanket of hair to keep them warm in the months to come.

The few calves that are born during this season sport the distinctive reddish-yellow hair of babyhood. Those born in the summer are already

The light-colored calf, photographed in October, was born in late summer.

a dark brown color, and the characteristic hump is much more noticeable now, especially on the young bulls. Their horns are only an inch or so in length—still not as impressive-looking as they will be later. These youngsters are eating grass along with the rest of the herd.

Many other animals share the bison's habitat. A good mammal book such as *A Field Guide to the Mammals* by W. H. Burt and R. P. Grossenheider contains excellent range maps that show the overlapping of the bison's range with that of almost every land mammal in North America. And a study of our native birds will reveal that an amazing number live on the bison's range. In addition there are many other creatures—reptiles, amphibians, fishes, insects—that live within the world of the bison. When we consider how many hundreds of species this continent supports, we begin to get an idea of the complexity of our natural world.

Among the most noticeable associates of the bison, of course, are the horned and antlered big game. By autumn, moose, elk, caribou, and other members of the deer family have their full growth of antlers. The velvet that covered them during their summer growth has been rubbed off, leaving them ready for the coming rutting-season battles.

The moose is the largest member of the deer family. During the moose's rutting season, which begins around the middle of September and lasts for about a month, the huge bulls roam about the woods looking for cows, and this is a good time to stay out of their way. While the moose did not live on most of the plains bison's range, it does share the habitat of the wood bison today.

The elk, our second largest deer, was at one time very much a plains animal, but the pressures of civilization drove it into the mountains, and it is now considered an animal of some of our roughest wildernesses. Its rutting season begins during the waning days of summer and lasts into the second week of October. It is then the shrill, high-pitched bugle of the bulls—one of the truly wild sounds of North America—can be heard.

Next in size among members of the deer family is the caribou, another species that shares the north country with the wood bison. It, too, has a

The bison shares its range with the moose and the elk.

The white-tailed deer and the pronghorn also live in bison country.

strong herding instinct, and bands of caribou numbering many thousands roam the far reaches of the continent. Autumn is its time to breed, mainly during October.

Both the white-tailed deer and the mule deer, probably the best-known species of big game in the country, live on the bison's range. Their rutting season begins in late October and lasts into December. At this time, when the bucks are searching for does, more than one person has been surprised to find that the normally shy mule deer and the white-tailed deer bucks have become aggressive.

The big-game animal that has been in closest association with the bison for centuries is the pronghorn. This handsome, fleet-footed animal —often mistakenly called an antelope—once also totaled in the millions. But it, too, succumbed to the pressures of a civilization that could not afford to leave thousands of square miles of fertile land unfenced and uncultivated. Fortunately, conservation efforts saved the species from extinction, and today sizable herds of pronghorns can be seen grazing near bison herds in many of our parks and refuges.

Our large carnivores—the species we call predators—include the black bear, the grizzly bear, the bobcat, the cougar, the coyote and the wolf.* All of them are residents on some part of the bison's range.

The black bear is not a serious predator on other animals, since it prefers plant roots, insects, rodents, and other more easily obtainable foods. The only reference to black bears and bison that I found made it clear who was afraid of whom—and it wasn't the bison.

The grizzly bear is another matter. It is large; it is powerful; it does present a threat to bison. Records indicate the neck of a bison can be broken with a single swipe of this bear's paw. But the grizzly is not fast, and in any kind of race a healthy bison would have no trouble winning. If a grizzly were to surprise a bison in heavy brush, or could otherwise get

*The relationships of these predators to the bison are documented and discussed in the Living World books *The World of the Black Bear, The World of the Grizzly Bear, The World of the Coyote,* and *The World of the Wolf.—Editor's Note*

Two more wilderness residents: the black bear and the grizzly bear.

very close without being detected, I have no doubt that the bear could kill the bison, but such a situation does not occur too often.

A sick or injured bison is another matter, however, and a grizzly might easily catch a weakened animal. In his book, *The Great Buffalo Hunt,* Wayne Gard reported an instance of a witnessed grizzly attack on bison:

A veteran hunter in Dakota once watched a huge male grizzly attack a small herd of buffalo cows protected by five or six bulls. As the bear approached, the bulls closed ranks and lowered their horns. When the bulls charged, the bear struck one of them so hard with his paws that he broke the back of the bull, killing him instantly. But the other bulls used their horns so effectively that soon the bear crawled off with mortal wounds.

There seems to be a difference of opinion among authorities as to whether or not the grizzly is a minor predator on the bison. John James Audubon ranked the grizzly more dangerous than the wolf to bison, and was supported in this opinion by Ernest Thompson Seton. But the grizzly bear is not a common animal, and although it does appear in the same country as the bison, in such places as Yellowstone National Park, its predation today has no important effect on bison numbers.

The cougar, a large cat that prefers hilly, mountainous, or forested country to flat, open areas where it cannot use its stalking ability, does not prey much on bison except for the young animals, and then only in timbered country. The smaller bobcat feeds mainly on rabbits and rodents. Since it does not like carrion, it probably seldom eats bison. It might be able to kill an unprotected calf, but this would be unusual.

Few species have been more maligned than the coyote, another small animal. It has proved wise enough to survive year-round campaigns launched by our Federal government to trap, poison, shoot, and otherwise destroy it. As a predator on bison it must be considered unimportant, although it undoubtedly preys on any unprotected calves and weakened adult bison it can find. But why risk death on the points of horns or under hoofs when rodents and rabbits are satisfactory fare?

The cougar, the bobcat, and the coyote (opposite) do not prey on full-grown healthy bison.

The wolf is a magnificent animal. It is both fast and agile, and averages more than 100 pounds in weight, with records up to 175 pounds. A large animal, it may measure as much as three feet high at the shoulder and six feet long from muzzle to tail tip. Singly, the wolf is a dangerous foe; in a pack, it is formidable. Yet, with all its physical capability plus great intelligence, this animal is not always successful in hunting large animals like deer and moose, which can hold their own against a pack.

Many historians believe that the Great Plains once contained many, many wolf packs, some of which were always lurking near the outer edges of the bison herds, waiting to fall upon a careless or weakened animal. Carcasses left by hunters were devoured overnight. With the bison's habitat greatly reduced, the wolf seems to be the only predator that might have a significant effect on our present bison numbers—and this only in Alaska and northern Canada, where wolves live on the largest remaining bison range. William A. Fuller said in his report on the bison of Wood

101

Buffalo National Park, "The only animal for which there is direct evidence of predation on bison is the timber wolf."

There is some evidence that wolves may be a threat to bison populations. In a letter to me, J. B. Fitzgerald, Director of Game for the Yukon Territorial Game Department, wrote: "The bison in the Yukon only amount to a few—possibly under 12 in number—the wolves keep this number down considerably. Five animals were obtained in 1953 from Alaska and these were the beginning of the small herd in our Territory." And William A. Fuller reported that an analysis of the stomach contents of fifty-nine wolves taken in Wood Buffalo National Park in the years 1951–54 showed that 65 per cent of the food was bison. An analysis of sixty-three scats, Fuller noted, revealed that 86 per cent of those scats contained bison remains. In conclusion, he wrote, "The two independent lines of evidence indicate that bison forms the staple diet of the park wolves."

Yet there is another side of the story, and again I cite Fuller's excellent report. In eleven case histories of wolf kills, five victims were very old animals. In three, the victims were calves. The three remaining bison were handicapped—one by a terminal case of tuberculosis, the other two by an infected bullet wound and a possible broken leg. Direct quotes from some of these case histories are interesting. The first case cited is quoted in full:

On November 16, 1950, during a small slaughtering operation, the tracks of two calves and six wolves were observed within half a mile of camp. Since hunting had been going on for two weeks, and 73 buffalo had been killed, many of them cows, it is likely that the calves were orphans. After the party followed the tracks for about eight miles and emerged on a large prairie, they saw the wolves attacking a calf. Another calf was standing about 30 feet to one side, apparently unconcerned. On our approach the wolves took flight. This second calf was shot and proved to have been previously uninjured. The first calf was dead and partly eviscerated. The wolves had attacked its right shoulder, flank, and thigh, but had not hamstrung it. This example showed that wolves do not have an easy time, even with practically defenseless calves five to six months of age. The chase lasted at least eight miles, and an area at least 25 feet in diameter at the site of the final encounter was trampled flat, showing that the calf had put up a battle. It also demonstrated that bison not under actual attack by wolves pay no attention to them, nor do the wolves seem interested in more than one victim at a time.

The other two calves that were killed had old as well as fresh wounds, and there was evidence that in each instance the attacking wolves had had trouble killing the calf.

In the case of the adult bull that had tuberculosis, Fuller said, "That animal must have been a menace to any that came in contact with it. The wolves had actually performed a service in herd sanitation when they ended its career."

The usual conclusion of such studies of predator-prey relationships is that the victims were handicapped in some way. The predator is not usually fussy; it matters not whether the animal is the fattest four-year-old cow in the herd or an aged bull too weak to stand. In general, predation is a good thing, for it helps maintain a healthy population. Man has been slow to learn this; therefore predators often have a bad name. But eventually education will win out and predators will be accepted, not as a threat to the animal community but as a worthwhile and important part of our whole living world.

Ed Olson of Wood Buffalo National Park reflects the thinking of knowledgeable men today when he wrote me that "timber wolves take their toll, especially of the old and cripples. They also, and this hurts the most, on occasion take a heavy toll of the calf crop. We do control our timber wolf population but certainly we do not have any intention of eliminating them in the park."

Many other species that share the range of the bison influence its life in large and small ways. Smaller carnivores include the red fox, the badger, the lynx, the skunk, the weasel, the wolverine, the marten, the fisher, the black-footed ferret, and the raccoon. Many of these animals

Other neighbors of the bison: the wolverine and the prairie dog.

The bison's literally closest neighbor is the "buffalo bird."

prey upon the rodents and rabbits, which eat the plants of the range and thus compete with the bison for food.

The rodents are also well represented: the yellow-bellied marmot, the woodchuck, various ground squirrels, the chipmunk, the tree squirrel, the prairie dog, the gopher, mice, rats, and the porcupine, among others. J. Dewey Soper listed a total of at least 46 species of mammals that are ecological associates of the bison in Wood Buffalo National Park.

The list of birds is even more extensive. Soper included 217 species that live in Wood Buffalo Park, and at least one of these comes into very close contact with the bison—the cowbird, or "buffalo bird." It spends hours feeding on insects on the ground near bison or picking them out of the bison's hair. On the prairies and plains, many species of birds are common: the western meadow lark—the state bird of Oregon, Montana,

Feathered inhabitants of the range: the willow ptarmigan (below) and the noisy magpie (opposite).

Wyoming, North Dakota, Nebraska, and Kansas—the sage grouse in the southern part of the range, the ptarmigan in the north, and the sharp-tailed grouse in many places; the killdeer with its vibrant call, the red-tailed hawk, and the magpie, which, along with other carrion eaters, quickly cleans up any dead animals.

Probably the best-known reptile in North America is the rattlesnake; the western rattlesnake lives over most of the Great Plains, from Mexico

Poised for flight—the red-tailed hawk.

The Western rattlesnake commands a certain respect.

to Canada. Lizards and turtles are among the other reptiles found in bison country.

The bison's coat grows heavier through the autumn months. This new growth of longer, denser hair made robe hunters start seeking herds about the middle of October. Until mid-December, the choicest hides were taken; later in the winter the pelts looked worn and bleached, making them less desirable for robes.

Those who best know the taste of bison meat claim that autumn is the best time to obtain it. Indians, and later the white man, killed the animals during this season and made jerky—strips of dried meat that substituted for hard-to-find fresh meat.

Opinions vary as to the eating quality of bison meat, though most who have eaten it consider it excellent. Some even claim it is much better than beef. I have eaten bison steaks, roasts, ground meat, and tongue and could scarcely tell the difference, except for the ground meat, which seemed quite dry. I believe that both flavor and tenderness are influenced by the age and condition of the animal, just as these factors largely determine the eating quality of beef. If I could have all the bison meat I wanted, I doubt that I would ever miss beef.

Many private bison herds in the United States and in Canada are kept for the production of meat. During World War II, bison meat was not rationed and it was in great demand. In our affluent society today, people like to try new and different things and are willing to pay for them. Many meat markets now package bison meat as a specialty item. A large chain store in Oregon recently bought a number of young bison for its retail meat sections, and the demand exceeded the supply even though the prices per pound were about two and a half times the prices charged for the same cuts of beef.

In many places, especially in the Great Plains and on the eastern slope of the Rocky Mountains, restaurants specialize in bison meat, and one can see signs reading BUFFALOBURGERS instead of HAMBURGERS.

A specialty item in the West.

Everywhere there is activity as the natural world prepares for the most difficult season of the year. Some animals busily gorge themselves on berries, roots, and insects while they are still available. Others build up a supply of seeds, cones, and nuts for the long winter ahead. Beavers are cutting and hauling tree limbs into deep water before the ice comes, while the weasel, ptarmigan, and arctic fox prepare themselves by exchanging the browns of summer for the white of winter. Nature provides the bison and many other animals with a thickened pelt that will keep them warm when temperatures plummet.

Man must also make preparations for winter, but he still takes time to appreciate the glorious spectacle of the leaf-clad trees and shrubs that proudly wear the scarlets, burnished golds, and russets of autumn. Soon, however, the colors fade, the earth wears a crunchy blanket of leaves, and bared limbs and branches etch themselves sharply against the sky. How much shorter the days are—and colder! The raccoon and the bear take sanctuary in cozy dens; the marmot and the squirrel snuggle into underground homes. Early snows linger briefly, but soon will come the first of many that will pile up and last until spring. The bison, spurning shelter, pursues its daily routine, unaffected by the change of seasons.

112

Winter

By the time the shortest day of the year arrives on the range, winter has indeed taken hold. Nights are longer; the sun does not have time to warm up the day. In Wood Buffalo National Park, it will not rise on this winter solstice until after 9 A.M., and it will set before 3 P.M.

Weather in some parts of the bison's range has been severe for many weeks. For any animal not fully prepared, the below-zero temperatures and heavy snowfalls can be fatal: another sign of nature's continual process of eliminating the weak.

Cold saps energy, and only food will replace it. But the food is harder to find now and carnivores begin to feel the pinch of hunger as they spend more time and energy hunting. When the snow is deep, many animals must make great efforts to lunge through the drifts, and running down prey becomes increasingly difficult. Browsers such as bighorn sheep seek grass on high, wind-swept ridges. Moose can depend on their long legs to get them through deep snow in search of willow, aspen, or poplar trees to feed on. Other browsers congregate in dense woods, to nibble on twigs, or migrate to lower, more open areas where the snow has not piled up so much.

The bison? It takes winter just as it does everything else—head on. Domestic cattle often drift before a blizzard and eventually die from the cold, starvation, or suffocation under snowdrifts. But the bison faces into the storm, presenting the same lowered burly head and

113

Bighorn sheep wander wind-swept ridges in search of grass.

polished horns it uses to meet any threat. Being much more heavily covered on the front end, this animal is ideally built to cope with the severest winter conditions; even abnormally low temperatures or deep snow have little effect on a healthy adult bison. Exceptional severity can hasten the end for those that are old, injured, or disease-weakened.

In winter bison lead a much more sedentary life than they do during the other seasons, and their activity is less varied. The herds still move about early, as they do all year but, owing to the short days, it is later by the clock. Summer's long midday period of loafing is cut short or abandoned completely, especially in the north, because low temperatures, snow, and short days make it imperative for the animals to spend the daylight hours feeding. Snow eliminates the need to travel long distances to water.

J. Dewey Soper noted that bison in Wood Buffalo National Park do not move about much in winter and entire herds remain in one location for months at a time. He pointed out, however, that they stay in the meadows and plains that have extensive areas of lush feed. In listing various choice tracts that the herds frequent each winter, he gave their areas as 180, 150, 50, 40, 40, 70, 60, 110, and 70 square miles. A herd

Bison make the most of winter's brief daylight hours to feed.

The bison snowplows its way to food.

can remain in one of these large feeding areas all winter without seemingly reducing the food supply significantly.

Elk and domestic cattle paw through the snow with their front feet to find food—but not the bison. It uses its head—literally. Thrusting its nose down through the snow, it slowly and powerfully swings its head from side to side, clearing a path a few feet wide. This bulldozing, snowplow action leaves the grasses exposed, and the bison eats everything within reach. The process is then repeated, step by short step forward,

118

the path thus created exposing a lot of ground. I have spent many hours watching bison feeding in this manner, and, although I have read occasionally that bison also use their front feet to clear away the snow, I have never yet seen this done, and most authorities agree that only the head is used.

This continual snowplowing wears away much of the hair on the face, and by spring the bare spots will be noticeable. If there are frequent periods of thaw, followed by freezing temperatures, crust forms on the snow, and the hair on the sides of the face is worn off down to the

This animal wound up with a snowball hanging from its beard.

The "snow line" on this bison's face shows how deep the snow is.

hide. Sometimes even the hide is worn, cut, or sore, and it is possible that an animal will resort to pawing to get through the heavier crusts if its face is extremely irritated or raw.

Anyone who questions the ability of the bison to withstand the severe winter weather need only check the weather records of northern Canada and Alaska. In Wood Buffalo National Park, ice on the rivers and the first snowfall of any consequence arrive in October. Weeks before this, heavy frosts are common, and shortly afterward the rivers are frozen solid. Snow, not as deep as it is in many areas of North America, may accumulate to a depth of about four feet. Once winter sets in, it lasts six months—about as long a period as the other three seasons combined. Large lakes, such as Lake Athabasca, at the southeastern edge of the park, or Great Slave Lake, just north of it, remain solidly frozen from about the middle of November until as late as May, June, or even the first of July. Ice normally reaches a thickness of some five or six feet; on Great Slave Lake, it has measured seven feet.

Average Fahrenheit temperatures for the winter are: November,

120

5 degrees above zero; December, 11 degrees below zero; January, 12 below zero; February, 9 below zero; March, 2 above zero. These *are* averages, however, and it is not uncommon for temperatures to hover around 30, 35, or even 40 degrees below zero for extended periods of time from December into March.

And yet bison remain in this area, healthy and apparently contented, making no attempt to migrate southward to warmer climes. The fact that the animals thrive in this fierce cold contradicts the theory that bison migrate south in the fall to escape the rigors of winters in our northern Great Plains.

Not all of the bison's range is subject to such bitter weather; yet at least one location can be as bad. The wild herd in Alaska, in the Delta Junction area, 97 miles southeast of Fairbanks, faces the severe interior Alaska winters every year. The January average in Fairbanks is 12 degrees below zero, the same as for Wood Buffalo National Park, although the area is a little farther north.

All the other parts of the range seem to have much milder winters. The National Bison Range in Montana lists a January average of about 24 degrees above zero, with the low set at 36 below—mild compared to the cold farther north. The buffalo ranch in Yellowstone National Park cites a January average of 13 degrees above zero, with the lowest being 58 below zero. Custer State Park in South Dakota averages 22 above zero in January; the record low is 44 below. The Fort Niobrara Refuge in Nebraska has a January average of 21 above, with 38 below zero as the low. Wichita Mountain Refuge in Oklahoma has the warmest January average: 38 degrees above zero; the low, 16 below zero.

Picking the extremes of the bison's former range, we find that herds managed to thrive in temperatures that extended from 60 degrees below zero to more than 110 degrees above. Some parts of Texas have January averages in the 60s and July averages in the 80s, while areas in the north will have a 12-degrees-below-zero January average and a July average of 60 degrees above. Very wide extremes, yes—but bison

Unlike domestic cattle, bison can look out for themselves in winter. This bull feeds contendedly in a snow-covered meadow.

seem to do well regardless of where they are.

Yet we cannot say that severe winters do not affect these animals. If the snow is very deep, if temperatures drop very low, if thaws and following freezes are much more severe than usual, bison suffer, as do most of the wildlife that remains active throughout the season. One of the worst possible conditions is deep snow, followed by a warm period during which the upper layer of the snow melts, followed in turn by a hard freeze that causes a thick crust to form on the recently thawed surface snow. Bison cannot snowplow through the heavy ice crust to reach food. On the other hand, it breaks under their ponderous weight, leaving them floundering in deep snow, fighting a layer of ice with each step. The much lighter wolf, which can move easily on the frozen surface, finds bison much more vulnerable in winter than at any other time of year. Again, it is the weakened and handicapped among the herd that will tire and succumb first.

Nevertheless, the bison is better adapted to cope with this icy peril than many other animals, and by brute strength it can force a path through snows too deep for less powerful animals like deer. When making such a trail, one or two bison lead the way, cutting a narrow path which the entire herd, in single file, then follows. Other species that inhabit the same range as the bison welcome such trails.

There is some evidence that unusually large numbers of bison were lost in deep snows in the period from about 1820 to 1840. Historians are vague about these fatalities, mainly because they have to rely on recorded rumors, hearsay, and the tales of the Indians. Several mention, for example, that a small number of bison once inhabited northeastern Utah, a few of which were killed by early Mormon settlers near Great Salt Lake. During what seems to have been a very severe winter in about 1837–38, snow fell to "a depth of ten feet on the level" in that area, and the few bison that escaped starvation are said to have disappeared soon afterward.

Winter

Records from around Wood Buffalo National Park are equally vague. The bison of the Peace River area (a river that flows across the park from west to east) were almost entirely eliminated one winter sometime between 1820 and 1840 by a "tremendous snowfall, up to 14 feet deep," which piled snow up "over the backs of the bison." The animals died from suffocation. Historians credit this tremendous snowfall, not hunting, with the near-elimination of bison from this region.

J. Dewey Soper, on the other hand, mentioned that winter can sometimes actually help bison. There are many areas of Wood Buffalo National Park that are too soft and boggy for the animals to venture into during the warm months, even though the feed is lush and good. But in cold weather these boggy areas freeze solid, to form a solid decking over which the bison can walk, thus affording them access to the luxuriant vegetation.

As with many other wild animals, bison seem to have the ability to predict storms, and many reports indicate that they "point" a storm. Entire herds are said to stand or lie with their heads facing in the direction from which the storm eventually comes. This ability of bison to survive the roughest of our Great Plains winters prompted an old Indian chief to make a wise observation at a peace council meeting in 1867. It seemed rather foolish, he said, to kill off the bison, an animal that could look out for itself in the winter, just to make room for the white man's cows, which had to be sheltered and fed.

True as it is that healthy bison can look out for themselves, winter is not a merciful season, and it is often the end of the road for those that are not completely healthy. This applies to all wildlife. An animal that might manage for months during the warm summer, even though greatly handicapped by a broken leg or disease, often cannot survive a long spell of cold weather.

A calf born in the fall might not be big or strong enough to fight the drifts and the cold temperatures of winter—or one born very early in the spring might not survive if the weather does not moderate soon

125

Despite the fact that bison are gregarious, the herds remain remarkably disease-free.

enough. But newborn bison are rugged; there are records of calves born in 38-below-zero weather that survived without apparent difficulty.

Many persons have observed that bison are usually disease-free. This is remarkable for such gregarious creatures, since it would seem logical for a sick animal to spread illness or disease to the rest of the herd.

Bison, however, are susceptible to some of the diseases of our domestic

126

cattle, though usually not as severely. Tuberculosis is one of the most prevalent diseases that afflicts the herds in Wood Buffalo National Park, but it is not found in those in the United States. Records from the past show no evidence of this sickness among wild animals, so it seems to be making its first appearance in captive animals. (There are three recognized forms of tuberculosis: bovine, avian, and human. Especially with the bovine and human types, cross-infection is possible, but humans can contract it only through close contact with infected animals.)

According to William A. Fuller, approximately 40 per cent of the bison in Wood Buffalo National Park are infected with tuberculosis. Over a period of five years, from 1952 through 1956, a total of 1,508 animals of all age groups were examined. Calves showed the lowest incidence, with only 15 per cent having the disease. The rate was greater among older animals: 56 per cent of them were diseased.

When a bison is infected, a small internal lesion forms, and at that time the animal develops a slight resistance to further reinfections. If the lesion erodes into a blood vessel, the disease enters the blood stream and progresses rapidly, causing death. If it does not erode into a blood vessel, the disease remains chronic and does not reach the fatal stage for several years. Most of the infected bison in Wood Buffalo National Park have chronic tuberculosis, and the annual mortality from it is rated at only 4 or 5 per cent.

Brucellosis, a disease common in cattle, was first diagnosed in bison in 1917, when blood samples were taken from animals in Yellowstone National Park. It was also discovered in the Wood Buffalo National Park herds in 1956, and by 1958 about 45 per cent of the animals were infected.

At first, infected bison show symptoms similar to those observed in cattle, but they apparently adapt later—further evidence of their ability to fight off disease. During the early period of infection, a majority of bison pregnancies end in abortion. Once the animals become conditioned to the disease, and even though the bison herd retains the infection, calves born later can be as healthy as those in a noninfected herd.

Bison are affected by other ills such as arthritis, arteriosclerosis, ophthalmia, cancer, pneumonia, and mange, but none of these appears to be cause for major concern. Other diseases, rarely found, have been recorded but are of even less importance.

Anthrax has been known to exist in livestock in North America since the early 1700s. It has also been reported in deer in California, Florida, Louisiana, and Texas, and in moose in Wyoming. Historians believe that it existed in bison a long time ago, but its occurrence has been rare in recent years.

In the last few years, however, it has proved potentially dangerous to the Wood Buffalo National Park herds. It was during a visit to the park in the summer of 1967 that I learned the disease had broken out. Because it is so highly infectious, some areas of the park were off limits that season. Canadian Wildlife Service personnel and government pathologists were at work there, attempting to control the disease and eliminate all possible sources of re-infection. Great care was being taken to prevent its spread. Anthrax bacteria are killed by heat, and all dead animals were being burned and buried; the areas around them burned and limed.

Nowhere in Canada was this disease ever reported in any wildlife species, including bison, until the Summer of 1962, when G. B. Kolenosky, while on a range-sampling helicopter flight in Wood Buffalo Park, noted thirty-two dead bison in two meadows. They were found on the east side of the Slave River, about 15 miles outside the northeast boundary of the park. More dead animals were found in the next twenty-four days, and of course they were examined to determine the cause of death. It proved to be anthrax.

That year, a total of 281 bison died of the disease in a 700-square-mile area between the Slave River on the west and the Taltson River on the east. It was estimated that the total bison population in that area at that time was about 1,300 animals. It was easy to single out for study the

The strongest survive the winter to carry on the species.

animals that were ill: whereas they should have been especially active— it was during the rutting season—they were apathetic and gaunt-looking. Most of the time they just stood around with lowered heads; when they walked, it was with difficulty; some even staggered. After this particular outbreak was checked, the disease seemed to vanish, only to reappear five years later. It is hoped that the control measures employed in 1967 will eliminate the disease.

Bison, like other species, are susceptible to the varieties of injuries sustained in accidents: broken bones, blindness caused by various mishaps, wounds resulting from mating season battles or the animals' customary slam-bang actions.

Death by drowning sometimes occurs in winter. When ice on rivers and lakes is not strong enough to support the weight of many bison, these convenient highways turn into death traps. Historians have cited many instances of such drownings. In an article written for the *Annual Report U. S. National Museum (1887)*, William T. Hornaday told about a herd of nearly a hundred animals in Minnesota that perished after breaking through ice.

Blizzards have also brought death to large numbers of bison. In the records is an account of a herd of about 100,000 bison that stampeded during a blinding snowstorm and accidentally plunged over a cliff.

But winter does not last forever, though some residents of the north sometimes feel that it will never end. Spring comes, almost unnoticed at first, then with bursts of color and new life.

Bison and Man

IT WAS MAN who nearly exterminated the bison; it was man who prevented its annihilation. This apparent paradox can be explained by the fact that man has the ability to sometimes see and correct his mistakes. He could not save the passenger pigeon because he did not see his error in time. But that species, which needed vast oak forests in order to survive, would have eventually disappeared anyway. We can be thankful that the bison exists today as more than a memory and a mounted specimen in museums.

A very large bison skull I found in Wood Buffalo National Park.

Little if any thanks, however, are due legislators of the late 1800s and early 1900s for the fact that some bison were saved—their efforts were ineffectual. The majority of bison at the turn of the century were in privately owned herds, whence came our present-day herds.

Even though it has been saved from extinction, the bison can never be restored to its former numbers because it is a wilderness animal—not the wilderness most of us visualize, with tall, snow-capped peaks and endless miles of giant timber, but a wilderness of grass, such as the Great Plains was a hundred years ago. The bison, in order to survive in great numbers as it did before, would once again have to command those seemingly limitless prairies and plains. But man can never relinquish so vast an area to a burly, humpbacked wild ox. The Great Plains is prime agricultural land, just as good for growing corn or grass for domestic cattle as it once was for growing the lush grasses upon which millions of bison fed.

Except for those in Wood Buffalo National Park in Canada, there are almost no truly wild bison left: a few in Alaska, the Yukon, Utah, Arizona—and these token herds number in the mere hundreds. Only in Alaska and Canada is there room for vast herds.

Nearly every state in the Union has some bison—in zoos, roadside animal farms, private ranches, parks, and refuges. Actually, they now live in areas they never before inhabited before the wholesale slaughter of the 1800s began. I have, for example, seen them in such diverse places as San Diego; alongside an interstate highway between Portland, Oregon and Seattle, Washington; in the spruce and muskeg country of interior Alaska; and running wild in Arizona. Bison can also be seen in Hawaii, New York City, Massachusetts, Michigan, New Hampshire, Maine, and even on islands off the coasts of South Carolina and Newfoundland—all places where the bison did not originally live. In addition, of course, they can be seen in major zoos throughout the world.

Anyone who wants to see bison under conditions that most closely approximate those under which the animals lived before the white man

Annual roundup time on the National Bison Range.

took over the land should visit one of the larger refuges or parks: the Wichita Mountains National Wildlife Refuge in Oklahoma; Fort Niobrara National Wildlife Refuge in Nebraska; Wind Cave National Monument or Custer State Park in South Dakota; Yellowstone National Park in Wyoming, Montana, and Idaho; the National Bison Range in Montana; Elk Island National Park in Alberta, Canada; or Wood Buffalo National Park in Alberta and the Northwest Territories.

To see wood bison, one must travel to Canada's northland, to Wood Buffalo National Park, where both the pure wood bison and a hybrid cross between the wood bison and the plains bison live.

At one time, even comparatively recently, knowledgeable biologists doubted the existence of wood bison in that vast and still largely unex-

133

plored area called the Northwest Territories. Indeed, such a creature seemed to many people to be nothing more than a legend. The first white man to discover the wood bison was the English explorer, Samuel Hearne, who came upon a herd of them in Canada on June 9, 1872. But many people continued to doubt their existence, especially as a separate subspecies.

In March, 1892, a bull was killed within 50 miles of Great Slave Lake and was scientifically described by Samuel N. Rhoads in 1897, thus officially establishing the existence of the wood bison. Rhoads pointed out that the wood bison is larger and darker than the plains animal and has certain skull and horn measurements that show it is a subspecies. For example, the distance between the bases of the horns is more than 50 mm. greater on the wood bison than it is on the largest old skull of a plains bison bull in the Academy of Natural Sciences in Philadelphia.

In the early 1900s it was believed that the wood bison, along with most of the plains bison farther south, had disappeared completely. It was not until after World War I, when a survey party in northern Alberta encountered a herd of several hundred bison, that hopes were renewed that the wood bison still lived. Efforts were made immediately to protect them, and Wood Buffalo National Park, established in 1922, became their refuge.

A few years later scientists were disturbed when an Ottawa official decided to increase the wood bison herds by importing many hundreds of plains bison from the south. These animals bred with the wood bison, and by 1949 many people felt sure that there were no true wood bison left. It came as a happy surprise when, in 1957, some wildlife officers who were taking an aerial census spotted a herd in a remote corner of Wood Buffalo National Park. The bison were at least 75 miles from the nearest known hybrid herd and separated from it by muskeg swamps and lakes. These animals were big and black, and immediately speculation began that a herd of pure wood bison had been found again.

In February and March of 1959, members of a land expedition went

Pure wood bison, believed to be extinct before a small herd was found in a remote corner of Wood Buffalo Park in 1957.

across country into that same part of the wilderness to attempt to establish the true identity of the animals. They discovered that the herd sighted in 1957 was definitely isolated from the other bison herds in the park, separated by extremely inhospitable country of a type not frequented by the bison. It was noted that they occupied the same area from which the original 1892 specimen of wood bison was taken.

Five specimens were obtained and carefully measured, their hides and bones preserved. Zoologists in Ottawa studied the measurements, and in 1960 they announced that about 200 pure wood bison did indeed exist in the wild state in a remote northwestern portion of Wood Buffalo National Park. I have seen some of these animals on my trips to the Northwest Territories, and it is obvious that they are larger and darker than the more common plains bison familiar to most of us.

Many persons—still believing that the bison is very close to extinction and that any and all animals should be carefully protected—are shocked to learn that bison are still being killed every year in most of the refuges, parks, and private herds.

The fact is that, in most areas, bison herds have grown to the maximum size supportable under the present range conditions. All wildlife and domestic livestock eventually reach such a limit, which is determined by the ability of the habitat to produce food and other necessaries for life. This is true of any given amount of land, be it large or small, and any surplus population must be removed or the land will deteriorate from overuse. Furthermore, with too many animals in one area, there is not enough food for all, and eventually some will suffer unless the surplus is eliminated. This problem is solved by wildlife and livestock management. A cattleman with two hundred acres of pasture knows how many cows he can feed on that land; any animals over that maximum must be sold or sent to slaughter. If he insists on having too many cows, the land will become overgrazed and as a result support fewer cattle.

Our native deer populations reproduce at a tremendous rate. Hunting must take care of this yearly growth or many of the deer will starve when the food supply is eaten up. And so it is with bison. They keep on reproducing; therefore the surplus—approximately equal to the number of young born each year—must be removed.

Some of the surplus animals are killed and the meat, hides, and skulls sold at auction. Other animals are sold alive to people interested in building up private herds. Of course, many private herds also reach their limits, and enough of these animals are disposed of to keep the numbers stable. With the growing demand for specialty meats in this country and good prices being paid for such cuts, there is a ready market for bison meat. In fact, some ranchers have switched from cattle to bison or have started bison herds to supplement their domestic livestock.

A few private ranches allow hunting for a fee, giving the trophy hunter an opportunity to shoot one of these shaggy beasts. In a few states—Arizona, Utah, Alaska—residents are allowed to hunt bison under the strict control of the local game departments.

Although no hunting is permitted within the boundaries of the Wood Buffalo National Park in Canada, the natives can hunt bison outside the park. One might think that, with boundaries unmarked and roads few, poaching would be a problem; fortunately, it is not. It might be difficult to explain to a hungry Indian that the bison should be saved for future generations when his own family is starving, but the natives of this region have been cooperative.

Many of the large bison herds in the United States are privately owned. Roy Houk of Fort Pierre, South Dakota, has a herd of about

Part of a private herd owned by Harry Pon of Burns, Oregon.

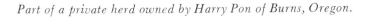

The author makes friends with a captive bison, which is as unpredictable as any wild one. (Photo by Ernie Kraft.)

1,400 animals. Harry Pon of Burns, Oregon, has nearly 1,000. In addition, there are scores of herds of various sizes in many parts of the United States and Canada.

Bison meat may be in demand, but there are more than a few problems involved in raising this animal. It has never liked fences and has never respected them. Ever since man began confining the bison, whether on private or public lands, it has shown its disdain for fences by walking through them. Nor are captive bison to be trusted any more than wild ones. They are equally difficult to handle and, in general, hard on the nerves of anyone who raises them.

This problem has led various people at various times to try to produce

138

A cattalo. Cross-breeding of bison and domestic cattle may yet prove successful.

a cross between bison and domestic cattle, in the hope that the resulting animals, termed "cattalo," would retain the better qualities of both species—i.e., the hardiness of the bison and the more gentle nature of the cow. Many attempts have been made, but so far the experiments have not been very successful. Too often the hybrid product of this mating has been sterile. Experimental cattle breeding takes time, effort, and money. In the future someone might produce an animal that is satisfactory on all counts, and then cattalo steaks might become a familiar item in our supermarkets.

It is customary for us to commemorate heroes—those men who have been important to the nation or a state. Presidents' faces appear on coins and stamps, their names on bridges and airports. Doctors, educators, and famed military men have places named in their honor. Important in the history and development of the country, such men are properly remembered.

The bison, too, has been honored in various ways. For many years the buffalo nickel was in common circulation in the United States, and even today a few can be seen. First minted in 1913, it helped to immortalize the bison; probably the best known of the various items which commemorate the bison, it is only one of many that do. A $10 bill issued in 1901 was engraved with the picture of a bison. A 30-cent stamp issued in 1923 used a similar picture.

State seals and flags, bottle labels, coins, and even a coat of arms—all have the bison as a symbol.

From 1929 until late 1968 the seal of the United States Department of the Interior featured a bison. The flag of Wyoming has a white bison on a field of blue, and the official state seals of Indiana and Kansas display the bison. During World War II, the U.S. 510th Tank Battalion used as its unit insignia a bison.

In Canada, the coat-of-arms of the province of Manitoba contains a bison, as does the official seal of the Royal Canadian Mounted Police. The head of the animal also appears on the beverage labels of the Calgary Brewing and Malting Company in Alberta.

140

This handsome statue, in Pioneers Park, Lincoln, Nebraska, honors American pioneers.

Pioneers State Park in Lincoln, Nebraska, contains a life-size statue of a fine-looking bison bull. Madras High School in Oregon, near the Warm Springs Indian Reservation, chose the white buffalo as its symbol, hoping the power of this animal, sacred to the Indians, would bring success to its athletic teams.

More than half of the fifty states in the United States, and many Canadian provinces, have some geographical features or place names honoring the bison, although "buffalo" is a more popular term; as far as I was able to learn, "bison" has been used in only five instances: Bison

141

Peak, Park County, Colorado; Bison Lake, Wood Buffalo National Park, Alberta, Canada; and the towns of Bison in Oklahoma, South Dakota, and Kansas.

On the other hand, "buffalo" has been used in at least thirty-three states and provinces to identify creeks, fords, forks, knobs, buttes, hills, peaks, points, ridges, islands, heads, lakes, bays, houses, mills, parks, stations, rapids, shoals, springs, ponds, wallows, licks, bayous, swamps, bottoms, coulees, flats, runs, paths, valleys, plains, crossroads, and meadows. At least twenty-two towns or cities are named Buffalo; there are three Buffalo counties. There is even a Buffaloville.

Some place names are more descriptive: White Buffalo Butte, Buffalo Chip Lake, Buffalo Hide Creek, Buffalo Horn Creek, Little Buffalo Creek, Buffalo Bull Knob, and Buffalo Hump.

From the city of Buffalo, New York, to the town of Buffalo Creek in northwestern Nevada, and from the Buffalo River in the Northwest Territories of Canada to Rio de las Vacas (River of the Cows) in Mexico, the bison is well represented in North America. Even our language reflects the influence of this animal: we use the word "buffalo" as a verb meaning to bluff or overawe.

Fortunately, the destruction of the largest of all North American land animals was brought to a halt before it was too late. Thus the bison should stand as a constant reminder that care must be taken not to eliminate a species from the face of the earth. Even though it may be too late to save some of the species now listed as being in danger of extinction, much is being done to help others than can still be helped—for example the extremely rare ivory-billed woodpecker, the whooping crane, and the California condor.

Yet, in his efforts to control one animal—be it insect or predatory mammal—man continues to endanger other animals. Our government still uses poisons, traps, and guns to kill so-called "pest" species of wildlife. Many prairie dog colonies have been poisoned off because these little creatures eat grasses that man needs for his cattle. If the prairie dog is eliminated, or even greatly reduced in number, the rare black-footed ferret will become extinct because its diet consists mainly of prairie dogs.

As a result of the continual war that is being waged against our larger predators, the wolf is gone from most of the United States outside of Alaska; thousands of coyotes and bobcats are poisoned and trapped each year; and the cougar, which helps reduce overpopulations of deer, has been brought close to extinction over much of its former range. There are times when predation must be curbed, but not by means of large-scale poisoning programs that will get rid of the predators—but will kill biologically useful animals as well. Many people, seeming not to understand that certain predators perform a useful service, exert political pressures to have them eliminated. Since the wolf was driven from Yellowstone National Park, elk numbers have increased to such an extent that the depleted food supply over much of the park's wildlife range has created a serious problem. It is encouraging that a small pack of wolves has been seen in the park since 1969. Their appearance may presage the return of wolves to that area and the needed natural control of the elk population.*

Extermination programs are risky undertakings because there exists in nature a balance that should not be unwittingly or willfully upset. Conservation efforts must therefore be based on knowledge of the conditions that are necessary for the survival of all living things—plant and animal—in a given environment. Ecology, the study of the relationships of such organisms to their environments, provides that knowledge.

Sometimes a relationship is obvious; at other times it is very difficult to discern. For example, how are the pigmy shrew, our smallest mammal, and the bison, our largest, involved with one another? The shrew eats grasses, upon which the bison also feeds. Other creatures in the environ-

---

*Editor's Note: In our Living World book *The World of the American Elk,* by Joe Van Wormer, the relationship between wolves and elk is considered.

ment play parts, too: shrews also eat grasshoppers, which coyotes include in their diet. And the coyote eats both shrew and bison, the latter mostly as carrion. Of course the dead and decaying carcasses of bison and other animals replenish the soil, thus furnishing more grass for shrews and bison. And so the cycle continues.

Ecology is a fascinating subject through which we can learn the purpose and value of everything in the near and far corners of our world. A plant that is not important in the diet of one species may sustain another. Or it may be taking up space that could be used by more valuable grasses or other plants. It may have uses not immediately evident to man, but no bison with an itch will deny the value of a rough-barked pine tree, even if it does not provide food! Even a rock on the plains, seemingly without use or meaning, may be vital to the life or death of some living organism.

And so, while the history of the bison during the past 150 years is in part a shameful account of wanton killing that nearly destroyed the species, it may help educate man to the threat that he represents to other creatures that he considers enemies or competitors. Let us hope that he has truly begun to learn how tragic—for himself, for our country, for all wildlife—is the disappearance of one native animal from our wild landscape.

Bison Classification

THE BISON is a vertebrate in the phylum Chordata because it has a back-bone. It is in the class Mammalia because it has body hair and suckles its young, which are born alive. It is in the order Artiodactyla because it is even-toed, and it belongs to the family *Bovidae* because it is a hollow-horned ruminant. Its genus name is *Bison*, its species name is *bison*.

There are two separate subspecies of bison in North America: the plains bison, *Bison bison bison* (Linnaeus), and the wood bison, *Bison bison athabascae* (Rhoads). In the past, other forms recognized were

The plains bison, Bison bison bison.

the northern bison, the Pennsylvania bison, the mountain bison, and the Oregon bison. The northern and the Pennsylvania bison are now considered to be identical with the plains bison; the mountain and the Oregon bison are now considered to be identical with the wood bison.

Another species of bison—the aurochs, sometimes called the wisent or European bison, *Bison bonasus*—lives in Europe. This animal is taller than, but not nearly as heavily built as, the American bison. Two great world wars have nearly eradicated the European bison; only a few exist today, mainly in parks and zoos.

The wood bison, Bison bison athabascae.

Some of the bison specimens in the Denver (Colorado) Museum of Natural History. The horns on the right, from an ancient Pleistocene bison, have a spread of about six feet.

The bones of other bison that lived in ancient times are being dug up in many areas of North America. As is true of many other extinct species, those bison were tremendous beasts; some had horns that measured seven feet across. Many natural history museums have the ancient skulls, and even entire skeletons, on display.

148

Bibliography

Allen, Arthur C., "The North American Bison: Juggernaut of the Plains." Unpublished report of in-service trainee of the National Park Service. March, 1967.

Allen, Durward L., *The Life of Prairies and Plains*. New York, McGraw-Hill Book Company, 1967.

Allen, Joel A., *The American Bisons, Living and Extinct*. Cambridge, Mass., Harvard University Press, 1876.

————, *History of the American Bison*. U.S. Government Printing Office, Washington, D.C., 1877.

The American Buffalo, Washington, D.C., U.S. Department of the Interior, Conservation Note 12, 1962.

Anthony, H. E., *Animals of America*. Garden City, N.Y., Garden City Publishing Company, 1937.

Bailey, Vernon, *The Mammals and Life Zones of Oregon*. Washington, D.C., U.S. Department of Agriculture, 1936.

Banfield, A. W. F., and N. S. Novakowski, *The Survival of the Wood Bison (Bison bison athabascae, Rhoads) in the N.W.T.* Ottawa, National Museum of Canada, Natural History Papers #8, 1960.

Boone and Crockett Club, *Records of North American Big Game*. New York, Holt, Rinehart, and Winston, 1964.

Bourlière, François, *The Natural History of Mammals*. New York, Alfred A. Knopf, 1954.

Boyd, M. F., "Occurrence of the American Bison in Alabama and Florida." *Science* (new series) 84:203 (1936).

Bryan, Pack, "Man and the American Bison." *National Wildlife* 2:1 (1964).

151

Burrell, Wesley R., "Buffalo Killer: Sharps." *Field and Stream* 61:59 (September, 1956).

Burt, William H., and Grossenheider, R. P., *A Field Guide to the Mammals*. Boston, Houghton Mifflin Company, 1952.

Cahalane, Victor H., *Mammals of North America*. New York, The Macmillan Company, 1947.

———, "Restoration of Wild Bison." *Transactions of the Ninth North American Wildlife Conference*. Washington, D.C., American Wildlife Institute, 1944.

———, "Buffalo Go Wild." *Natural History* 53:148 (April, 1944).

Choquette, L. P. E., "The Public Health Importance of some Diseases of Wildlife in Canada." Hanover, Germany, *Proceedings XVIIth World Veterinary Congress,* 1963.

———, J. F. Gallivan, J. L. Byrnes, and J. Piliparicius, "Parasites and Diseases of Bison in Canada. I. Tuberculosis and Some Other Pathological Conditions in Bison at Wood Buffalo and Elk Island National Parks in the Fall and Winter of 1959–60." *Canadian Veterinary Journal* 2:168 (1961).

Corner, A. H., and R. Connell, "Brucellosis in Bison, Elk and Moose in Elk Island National Park, Alberta, Canada." *Canadian Journal of Comparative Medicine and Veterinary Science,* 22:9 (1958).

Cousineau, J. G., "Wildlife and Some Diseases of Domestic Animals in Canada." *Canadian Veterinary Journal* 5:121 (1964).

Dickie, Francis, "Shades of the Buffalo; Branding Wood Bison." *Flying,* 57:34 (November, 1955).

Dobie, J. Frank, *The Voice of the Coyote*. Boston, Little, Brown & Company, 1949.

Froman, Robert, "Buffalo That Refused to Vanish." *Reader's Digest,* 72:195 (June, 1958).

Fuller, William A., "Aerial Census of Northern Bison in Wood Buffalo Park and Vicinity." *Journal of Wildlife Management* 14(4):445 (1950).

———, "Behavior and Social Organization of the Wild Bison of Wood Buffalo National Park." *Arctic* 13(1):2 (1960).

———, *The Biology and Management of the Bison of Wood Buffalo National Park*. Canadian Wildlife Service Wildlife Management

Bibliography

Bulletin, Series 1, No. 16:52 (1962).

Gard, Wayne, *The Great Buffalo Hunt.* New York. Alfred A. Knopf, 1959.

Garretson, Martin S., *The American Bison: Story of Its Extermination and Its Restoration Under Federal Protection.* New York, New York Zoological Society, 1938.

Goodwin, George G., "Coronado's Crooked-backed Oxen." *Natural History* 61:164 (April, 1952).

Hedlin, Ralph, "Bull of the North." *Field and Stream* 65:42 (June, 1960).

Hornaday, William T., "The Extermination of the American Bison, With a Sketch of Its Discovery and Life History." Washington, D.C., *Annual Report U.S. National Museum (1887), 1889.*

"How the True Cattalo is Bred." *Scientific American* 133:89 (August, 1925).

Kitto, F. H., "The Survival of the American Bison in Canada." *Geographical Journal* (London), LXIII:431 (1924).

Lake, Stuart N., "Buffalo Hunters; Interview with Wyatt Earp." *Saturday Evening Post* 203:12 (October 25, 1930).

McCracken, Harold, "Sacred White Buffalo." *Natural History,* 55:304 (September, 1946).

McHugh, Tom, "Social Behavior of the American Buffalo." *Zoologica* 43:1 (1958).

McNary, David C., "Anthrax in American Bison." *Journal of the American Veterinary Medicine Association,* 112(854):378 (1948).

Management of Buffalo Herds. Washington, D.C., U.S. Fish & Wildlife Service, Wildlife Leaflet 212, 1955.

Miller, Gerrit S., Jr., and Remington Kellogg, *List of North American Recent Mammals.* Washington, D.C., U.S. Government Printing Office, U.S. National Museum Bulletin 205, 1955.

Murie, Adolph, *Ecology of the Coyote in the Yellowstone.* Washington, D.C., U.S. Government Printing Office, U.S. Department of the Interior, Fauna Series No. 4 (1940).

Novakowski, Nicholas S., J. G. Cousineau, G. B. Kolenosky, G. S. Wilton, and L. P. E. Choquette, "Parasites and Diseases of Bison in Canada. II. Anthrax Epizooty in the Northwest Territories." Detroit, Mich., *Proceedings of the 28th North American Wildlife and Natural Resources Conference,* 1963.

————, and W. E. Stevens, "The Status of the Wood Bison in Canada." Winnipeg, Manitoba, *American Society of Mammalogists Conference Proceedings,* 1965.

Palmer, Ralph S., *The Mammal Guide.* Garden City, N.Y., Doubleday & Company, 1954.

Palmer, T. S., "Our National Herds of Buffalo." *Annual Report of The American Bison Society,* 10:40–62 (1916).

Peterson, H., "Buffalo Bill was a Piker; D. C. Basolo's One-day Record for Buffalo Kills." *Sports Illustrated* 21:76 (October 19, 1964).

Rhoads, Samuel N., "Notes on Living and Extinct Species of North American Bovidae." *Proceedings of the Academy of Natural Sciences of Philadelphia* 49:483 (1897).

Riley, Smith, "Buffalo, a Verb." *Nature Magazine* 23:185 (April, 1934).

Roberts, L., "Wild Wood Buffalo." *Outlook* 135:495 (1923).

Roe, Frank G., *The North American Buffalo: a Critical Study of the Species in Its Wild State.* Toronto, Canada, University of Toronto Press, 1951.

Rowley, Samuel R., "The Buffalo-Jumps of Montana." *Our Public Lands* 17(3):9 (1967).

Rutter, Russell J., and Douglas H. Pimlott, *The World of the Wolf.* J. B. Lippincott Company, Philadelphia, 1968.

Sandoz, Mari, *The Buffalo Hunters.* New York, Hastings House, 1954.

Seton, Ernest Thompson, *Lives of Game Animals.* Boston, Charles T. Branford Company, 1909.

Skinner, Morris F., and O. C. Kaisen, *The Fossil Bison of Alaska and Preliminary Revision of the Genus.* New York, Bulletin American Museum of Natural History 89(3):131 (1947).

Smith, Winston O., *The Sharps Rifle.* New York, William Morrow & Company, 1943.

Soper, J. Dewey, *History, Range, and Home Life of the Northern Bison.* Ottawa, Canada, Department of Mines and Resources, Ecological Monographs 2(4):347 (1941).

"White Buffalo, Big Medicine." *Scientific American* 150:96 (February, 1934).

Bibliography

Williamson, Glenn Y., "Story of the American Buffalo." *Science Digest* 20:57 (July, 1946).

Wold, Jo Anne, "Home on the Range." *Alaska Sportsman* 32(8):20 (1965).

Young, Stanley P., and Edward A. Goldman, *The Wolves of North America*. New York, Dover Publications, 1964.

Index

Index